MORE Reading Comprehension
in Varied Subject Matter

SOCIAL STUDIES

LITERATURE AND LANGUAGE

COMBINED SUBJECTS

PHILOSOPHY, LOGIC, AND MATH

SCIENCE   THE ARTS

JANE ERVIN

EDUCATORS PUBLISHING SERVICE
Cambridge and Toronto

TO THE STUDENT

Each selection in this workbook is on a theme which runs throughout the series. For example, Selection 5 in each book is about "Great Americans"; Selection 14 asks "What Do You Think?" while Selection 22 is on "Different Literary Forms and Styles."

There are also themes and topics within each book. These relate the selections to one another, show different aspects of a topic, and help you to gain a broader knowledge of a subject.

The topics in this book are what people are capable of: evil and love, the heart, food, and overcoming problems or hardships. Look for these topics, and how they are treated, as you read the selections.

1997 REVISED EDITION OF
READING COMPREHENSION BOOK 10

Educators Publishing Service
www.epsbooks.com
800.435.7728

Copyright © 1997, 1982, 1975 by Educators Publishing Service, a division of School Specialty Publishing, a member of the School Specialty Family. All rights reserved. No part of this book may be reproduced or utilized in any form or by any electronic or mechanical means, including photocopying, without permission in writing from the publisher.

Printed in U.S.A.
ISBN 0-8388-0609-0
978-0-8388-0609-8
9 10 11 PPG 10 09 08

CONTENTS

THE FALL OF TROY

ABOUT THE PASSAGE

More than 3,000 years ago, according to Greek mythology, the ancient Greeks fought the Trojans. The war went on for ten years and there seemed to be no way either side could win. Then the Greeks came up with a trick. They found a way to get inside the walled city of Troy, which would enable them to win the war.

What was this trick? Did this war really take place? Was there such a place as Troy, or was it just a mythological city?

REASON FOR READING

This passage is not difficult, but it is long. It gives you practice in following a writer's train of thought. Read it fairly quickly, keeping your concentration to the end. Decide if you think the Greeks' plan was actually executed.

READ THE PASSAGE

Priam, the King of Troy, was a powerful ruler who dominated the land and sea for miles around. Troy was situated at the entrance to a narrow channel of water that connects the Aegean Sea with the Black Sea. King Priam took advantage of this. He charged a toll whenever his enemies' (the Greeks) ships went by full of cargo. This infuriated the Greeks, who had to pass through this waterway to get to Asia for supplies of wheat and other food they were unable to grow on their rocky, hilly land. Why should they have to pay to use the channel, the Greeks asked. The sea is free. They vowed that if the Trojans continued this practice, there would be war. But King Priam was not **disconcerted.** There was a great stone wall around his city. No one—not even a Greek army—could get into Troy.

Finally, the tension erupted when the Trojans captured Helen, the wife of Menelaus (Men-uh-LAY-us), King of the Greek Kingdom of Sparta. The Greek armies banded together. The Greeks sacrificed a great bull to the sacred statue of Athena, goddess of war and wisdom, asking for her help. Odysseus, the strong, shrewd, and **wily** son of the King of Ithaca, was chosen as the leader. The army, together with armor, weapons, chariots, food, and horses, set off for Troy.

When the Greek ships were sighted, Priam and his men went to the temple to pray. They offered a sacrifice of a giant ram to the sacred statue of Athena, asking for her help.

The Greek ships landed on the shore near Troy, set up camp, and soon the battle began. The fighting continued—day after day, week after week, month after month. The war continued for an incredible ten years. The sides were equally matched; they were at an impasse. Finally, Odysseus realized that there was only one way for the Greeks to defeat Troy—they must **penetrate** the city. But how?

Odysseus pondered the question. Then, one day, inspiration came. Noticing the sturdy Greek ships near the shore, the thought struck him that no one could build ships like the Greeks; they could build anything. He came up with an **ingenious** plan. It was dangerous. If it failed, many Greeks would be killed. But if it succeeded, Troy would fall.

Ships were sent to nearby Greek islands where many trees were cut down and brought back. The skilled carpenters set to work immediately. They built a giant wooden frame, which was taller than the Trojan wall. The men wondered how it was to be used. They became even more curious when the construction took the form of a towering giant

---

* In this sample selection, some answers to the questions are omitted so students can answer them.

From *Mysteries of the Unknown: Mystic Places* by the Editors of Time-Life Books, © 1987, Time-Life Books, Inc.

horse. Its belly was hollow and there was a door on one side just big enough for a man to crawl through.

Odysseus's daring plan was that some of the soldiers would hide inside the horse. Meanwhile the rest of the Greeks would break up camp and head out to sea so the Trojans would think that, at last, the Greeks were giving up and returning home. However, instead of going home, the Greek ships would hide beyond the nearest island of Tenedos, where they would not be seen by the Trojans.

At last one night the plan was carried out. The next morning, looking out from the walls of their city, the Trojans were astounded to find the Greeks had gone. But they were even more astounded to find a monstrous, enormous, wooden horse in front of their gates. They gazed at it from every angle, wondering about its purpose. They were suspicious. Some said, "Destroy it." Others said, "Get rid of it into the sea." The Greek soldiers inside the horse heard all of this.

Then the Trojans discovered a Greek, named Simon, who had been left behind as part of Odysseus's strategy. He had been **primed** by Odysseus with **plausible** stories about the Greeks' departure, the wooden horse, and his own presence there. He told the Trojans that the Greeks left because they thought Athena had deserted them and they could not win without her help. He explained his presence by saying he had been chosen as a human sacrifice to guarantee the Greeks' safe journey home, but he had escaped and hidden. As for the horse, he said that it had been left to placate the angry goddess. The Greeks were hoping the Trojans would **desecrate** it and thereby earn Athena's hatred.

These lies convinced King Priam and the Trojans. They made the gate large enough for the wooden horse to be dragged through and maneuvered it to the center of the city. All day the Trojans celebrated their victory until eventually, full of food and drink, they fell asleep.

When all was quiet, the Greeks descended from the wooden horse. They opened the city gates to the Greek army, who had returned. They set fires throughout the city, massacred the inhabitants, and looted. The Trojan resistance was ineffectual. By morning, all but a few Trojans were dead, and Troy was devastated.

The ten-year war was over, but did it actually take place? Was there such a place as Troy?

The story of the Trojan war comes from a number of sources, mainly Greek and Roman poets and storytellers from the 12th century B.C. The best known source is the masterpiece written by the great Greek poet, Homer, called the *Iliad*. It is an epic poem that describes the exploits of the men fighting in the Trojan war, especially the Greek hero Achilles. The *Iliad* is valued both for the beauty of its language and its historical and archaeological richness.

Inspired after reading the *Iliad*, Heinrich Schliemann, "a nineteenth-century millionaire, amateur archeologist and a dreamer,"* proved that the story of the Trojan war was based on historical fact.

"Schliemann decided the Turkish town of Hissarlik, known for its fortress-like earth mounds, best matched the scene of the *Iliad*. In 1871, he began to dig, and soon he found that a city did indeed lie beneath Hissarlik's earthworks. In fact, several ancient cities were buried there, one atop the other. One of the layers, scorched by fire, looked very much like Homer's Troy.

"The excavation reached its peak on a morning in the summer of 1873. That day Schliemann prized golden necklaces, earrings, dishes, and more out of the hard-packed earth. He would later place the most spectacular piece, a gold diadem, on the brow of his Greek wife, Sophia, dubbing her 'my Helena'."*

Subsequent archeologists have confirmed that the city Schliemann unearthed is very probably the Troy that Homer wrote about. The story of Troy is no longer a myth, which raises the question, what other stories that are considered myths are really true?

---

* Quoted from *Mysteries of the Unknown: Mystic Places* by the Editors of Time-Life Books, © 1987, Time-Life Books, Inc., p. 18.

THINKING IT OVER

(1) What were the names of: The King of Troy: _____King Priam_____

The King of Sparta: _____King Menelaus_____

(2) What were the two causes of the war? _____

_____

_____

(3) Why was one Greek man left behind when the Greek ships left? _____

_____

STUDYING THE PASSAGE

(1) Find the Main Idea: Choose one.
   (a) The destruction of Troy.
   (b) The ten-year war.
   (c) How the Greeks tricked the Trojans.
   (d) A mythical story that seems likely to be true.   _____

(2) Find the Facts: Mark each one *true* or *false*.
   (a) The Greeks' land was very fertile.   _F_
   (b) Athena was the goddess of war and wisdom.   _T_
   (c) Both the Greeks and the Trojans believed Athena's help was crucial to their success. _____
   (d) The Greeks cut down the trees near their camp to build the wooden horse.   _____
   (e) The Greek ships hid behind a nearby island.   _____
   (f) Simon convinced the Trojans with his stories.   _____
   (g) Homer was a Trojan who wrote about the war.   _____
   (h) The city of Troy is believed to be in Turkey under the town of Hissarlik.   _____

(3) Find the Order: Number the following in the order in which they appear in the passage.
   (a) The sides were equally matched.   _3_
   (b) They were even more astounded to find a monstrous, enormous, wooden horse.   _5_
   (c) When all was quiet, the Greeks descended from the wooden horse.   _6_
   (d) They built a giant wooden frame.   _____
   (e) That day Schliemann found a spectacular gold diadem.   _____
   (f) But King Priam was not disconcerted.   _____
   (g) The story of Troy comes from a number of sources.   _____
   (h) A sacrifice of a great bull was made to the sacred statue of Athena.   _____

(4) Go beyond the Facts: The success of Odysseus's plan depended on all of the following except:
   (a) Simon's credibility.
   (b) The Trojans' belief in the power of the gods.
   (c) The Trojans' belief their city walls were impenetrable.
   (d) The belief at the time that a horse had magical powers.   _d_

3

(5) Determine the Writer's Style and Technique: The writer:
   (a) Tries to persuade you to believe that Troy existed.
   (b) Factually recounts the story of the fall of Troy and its later discovery.
   (c) Uses questions and answers to tell the story of Troy.
   (d) Tells the story of Troy through dramatizing it.   _____

USING THE WORDS

(1) Words and Their Meanings: Find the boldfaced word for these definitions.

ingenious	(a) clever, or skillful, as at inventing things
plausible	(b) seems to be true or possible
wily	(c) cunning; crafty; full of sly tricks
_____	(d) to stop from being angry; make peaceful; soothe feelings
_____	(e) pass through, enter
_____	(f) to use something sacred in a wrong or bad way; treat as if not sacred
_____	(g) made ready; prepared beforehand
_____	(h) brought confusion or disorder to; upset

(2) Write a paragraph using four of the words from the list above. Use a separate piece of paper.

WRITING ABOUT IT

Use a separate piece of paper.

(1) Working with a group of your classmates, or with the help of your teacher, write a scene for a play about the Trojan war. In this scene, the wooden horse has just been completed and the men are wondering how Odysseus intends to use it. Then Odysseus outlines his plan and the men react in different ways. Simon is chosen, or volunteers, to be the man left behind. At the end of the scene, some of the soldiers climb into the horse, while the rest prepare to leave.

   As you plan the scene, try to put yourself in the Greek soldiers' position. Remember they have been fighting for ten years in a foreign land.

(2) Write a myth in which an animal (it may be a real animal or a constructed one like the wooden horse) "saves the day."

4

THE LOVE BETWEEN A MOTHER AND A SON

ABOUT THE PASSAGE

Sure there is no love greater than the love between parents and their children. How do you think they would communicate this love if they knew they were probably seeing each other for the last time; as is the case in this passage?

REASON FOR READING

Notice how Remarque, in his powerful book, *All Quiet on the Western Front*, conveys the deep love between the soldier, on leave from the war, and his dying mother. Does he accomplish this through spoken words, their thoughts, or their actions?

READ THE PASSAGE

What is leave? A pause that only makes everything worse. Already the sense of parting begins to **intrude** itself. My mother **watches** me silently; I know she counts the days; every morning she is sad. It is one day less. She has put away my pack; she does not want to be reminded by it. . . .

It is the last evening at home. Everyone is **silent**. I go to bed early, I seize the pillow, press it against myself and bury my head in it. Who knows if I will ever lie in a feather bed again?

Late in the night my mother comes into my room. She thinks I am asleep, and I pretend to be so. To talk, to stay awake with one another, it is too hard.

She sits long into the night although she is in pain and often **writhes.** At last I can **bear** it no longer, and pretend I have just wakened up.

"Go and sleep, Mother, you will catch cold here."

"I can sleep enough later," she says.

I sit up. "I don't go straight back to the front, Mother. I have to do four weeks at the training camp. I may come over from there one Sunday, perhaps."

She is silent. Then she asks gently: "Are you very much afraid?"

"No, Mother."

"I would like to tell you to be on your guard against the women out in France. They are no good."

Ah! Mother, Mother! You still think I am a child—why can I not put my head in your lap and weep? Why have I always to be strong and self-controlled? I would like to weep and be comforted too, indeed I am little more than a child; in the **wardrobe** still hang short, boy's trousers—it is such a little time ago, why is it over?

"Where we are there aren't any women, Mother," I say as calmly as I can.

"And be very careful at the front, Paul."

Ah! Mother, Mother! Why do I not take you in my arms and die with you? What poor wretches we are!

"Yes Mother, I will."

"I will pray for you every day, Paul."

Ah! Mother, Mother! Let us rise up and go out, back through the years, where the burden of all this misery lies on us no more, back to you and me alone, mother!

"Perhaps you can get a job that is not so dangerous."

"Yes, Mother, perhaps I can get into the cookhouse, that can easily be done."

"You do it then, and if the others say anything—"

"That won't worry me, mother—"

She sighs. Her face is a white gleam in the darkness.

"Now you must go to sleep, Mother."

She does not reply. I get up and wrap my cover round her shoulders.

She supports herself on my arm, she is in pain. And so I take her to her room. I stay with her a little while.

"And you must get well again, Mother, before I come back."

"Yes, yes, my child."

"You ought not to send your things to me, Mother. We have plenty to eat out there. You can make much better use of them here."

How **destitute** she lies there in her bed, she that loves me more than all the world. As I am about to leave, she says hastily: "I have two pairs of underpants for you. They are all wool. They will keep you warm. You must not forget to put them in your pack."

Ah! Mother! I know what these underpants have cost you in waiting, and walking, and begging! Ah! Mother, Mother! how can it be that I must part from you? Who else is there that has any claim on me but you? Here I sit and there you are lying; we have so much to say, and we shall never say it.

"Good-night, Mother."

"Good-night, my child."

The room is dark. I hear my mother's breathing, and the ticking of the clock. Outside the window the wind blows and the chestnut trees rustle.

On the landing I stumble over my pack, which lies there already made up because I have to leave early in the morning.

I bite into my pillow. I grasp the iron rods of my bed with my fists. I ought never to have come here. Out there I was **indifferent** and often hopeless—I will never be able to be so again. I was a soldier, and now I am nothing but an **agony** for myself, for my mother, for everything that is so comfortless and without end.

I ought never to have come on leave.

THINKING IT OVER

(1) Why does the soldier think he should not have come home on leave? _____

_____

_____

(2) What deeper meaning is there in the soldier's thought, "Who knows if I will ever lie in a feather bed

again"? _____

STUDYING THE PASSAGE

(1) Find the Main Idea: Choose one.
   (a) A soldier's last night at home.
   (b) A son's sadness about his mother's illness.
   (c) The deep, unsaid love between a mother and a son.
   (d) A young man's love for his family. _____

(2) Find the Facts: Mark each one *true* or *false*.
   (a) Each morning the mother is happy knowing she has another day with her son. _____
   (b) The soldier stays up late to enjoy his last day to the end. _____
   (c) His mother comes in when he is asleep. _____
   (d) The mother sits for a long time by his bed although she is in pain. _____
   (e) The soldier says he has four more weeks before he goes to the front. _____
   (f) The soldier says he is not afraid. _____
   (g) The soldier is a young man, barely more than a boy. _____
   (h) The mother has gone to inordinate ends to give her son two pairs of underpants. _____

(3) Find the Order: Number the following in the order in which they appear in the passage.

(a) Why can I not put my head in your lap and weep? _____

(b) Ah! Mother, Mother! how can it be that I must part from you? _____

(c) Late in the night my mother comes into my room. _____

(d) I get up and wrap my cover round her shoulders. _____

(e) I seize the pillow, press it against myself and bury my head in it. _____

(f) "I will pray for you every day, Paul." _____

(g) "I can sleep enough later," she says. _____

(h) Already the sense of parting begins to intrude itself. _____

(4) Go beyond the Facts: Which two of these sentences from the passage sums up what Remarque is trying to convey in this passage?

(a) She that loves me more than all the world.

(b) How can it be that I must part from you?

(c) We have so much to say, and we shall never say it.

(d) I ought never to have come on leave. _____ _____

(5) Determine the Writer's Style and Technique: How does Remarque convey the deep love between the mother and the son? Choose two.

(a) By what they say to each other.

(b) Through both their thoughts.

(c) Through the thoughts of one of them.

(d) Through their actions. _____ _____

USING THE WORDS

(1) Words and Their Meanings: Find the boldfaced word for these definitions.

_____ (a) inaudible; tacit

_____ (b) a closet or cabinet to hang clothes in

_____ (c) scrutinize

_____ (d) very poor; being without

_____ (e) having or showing no interest or concern; unmoved

_____ (f) to twist and turn; squirm

_____ (g) tolerate; endure

_____ (h) terrible mental or physical pain

(2) Write a paragraph using four of the words from the list above. Use a separate piece of paper.

WRITING ABOUT IT

Use a separate piece of paper.

(1) Describe a deep love between two people who have to part—one of the "characters" can be yourself.

(2) Make up a poem entitled "Love."

7

THE POWERFUL RIVER*

ABOUT THE PASSAGE

One of the most efficient transportation systems in the world is very close to home—inside of us. It is our cardiovascular system.

How long does it take for a drop of blood to circulate throughout your body?

(a) About a second
(c) About a minute
(b) About 30 seconds
(d) About 5 minutes

REASON FOR READING

To practice reading for details and following a logical sequence of events.

READ THE PASSAGE

Within the human body flows a river unlike any other earthly river—a crimson stream that courses through every organ, twists past every cell on a journey that stretches sixty thousand miles, enough to circle the planet two and a half times. Earthly rivers refresh the land with water; the body's stream nourishes and cleanses, delivering food and oxygen to every cell, removing waste, regulating the human environment. Earth's rivers flow through inorganic rock and sand; the body's river travels through living tissue. The powerful heart that propels this stream and the vessels that guide it are all alive. The human river can regulate its own **velocity,** its banks widening or narrowing to control the shifting tides. And it can change its own course, instantly channeling its swift currents to meet new demands: swimming or sleeping, contemplating, celebrating, running a race or rocking an infant—each alters the flow of this powerful river.

The Life-Giving Loop

Every 60 seconds, 1,440 times a day, our blood cycles through the body; traveling the double loop—from heart through lungs and from heart through body—known as the cardiovascular system. Fresh, oxygenated blood begins its voyage to the body's tissues by bursting from the left side of the heart into the arching aorta, the body's largest artery. Even the average resting heartbeat hurls about two ounces of blood against the aorta walls

with great force. These tidal waves of blood smash against the aorta 70 times a minute, delivering their blows 2–5 billion times during the average life span.

Rigid metal pipes could not withstand this battering for long, but the living tissues of our blood vessels have evolved with just this function. Artery walls have three layers: a smooth inner lining, a thick middle layer of elastic membranes and muscle, and an outer layer of fibrous connective tissue. The aorta's elastic membranes stretch with the impact of each surge of blood; its strong muscle fibers then recoil, channeling the **intermittent** waves into one continuous stream. The resilient muscles also act as a subsidiary pump, propelling blood through our larger arteries at a rate of one foot a second.

As arteries divide and subdivide, the elastic membranes in their walls **diminish,** and the proportion of muscle grows. A single muscle cell may wrap two or three times around each of the smallest arteries, the last short branches of the arterial tree. Rhythmically squeezing and relaxing, these muscled rings force blood into the ten billion capillaries that fan throughout the body.

Most tissues—brain, intestine, heart, blood vessel—are laced with so dense a network of capillaries that no cell lies more than a millionth of an inch from a blood supply. Capillaries, with **gossamer** walls only one cell thick, are so fine that even red cells must bend and twist to squeeze, one at a time, through their narrow **straits.** Yet these vessels perform the cardiovascular system's vital task: they replace waste and carbon dioxide with oxygen and nutrients, delivering life to the cell.

Capillaries deliver their cargo by maintaining a precise balance of pressures between the blood flowing within their walls and the fluid in and around the body's cells. Arterioles pump blood into the capillaries with force sufficient to drive plasma—the fluid of the blood—and its dissolved nutrients through **porous** capillary walls. Cells, busily combusting nutrients to create energy, have a lower concentration of oxygen than the blood in capillaries. This tissue fluid hungrily sucks oxygen out of the red cells' iron grip and through the capillary membrane. Inside the capillary, blood cells and plasma proteins too large to pass through the vessel walls travel on in the thickened stream.

A Delicate Balance

Now the process of **osmosis** takes over. Water laden with carbon dioxide diffuses from the tissues into the capillary's **dehydrated** plasma. In one minute the water in blood plasma changes place with tissue liquids forty-five times. Still, our blood volume remains constant, thanks to the equilibrium between blood pressure, which forces fluid out of capillaries, and osmotic pressure, which sucks it in. If we lost this balance—if we lost our plasma proteins with their osmotic attraction—the liquid in our bloodstream would quickly and irretrievably flow into body tissue.

By the time blood leaves the capillaries, the swift current propelled by the heart and muscled arteries has slowed to less than a fraction of an inch a second. Bluish blood, laden with carbon dioxide and other wastes, flows sluggishly into the body's veins for the return trip to the heart and lungs. Equipped with fewer muscles than the arteries, veins cannot pump blood as vigorously as arteries do. This is especially true of veins that carry blood uphill from the feet. The thin-walled, elastic veins oppose gravity by relying on the body muscles that surround them. Whenever we move, muscles of the leg, arm, and even stomach press against the veins, sending blood on its way. In addition, one-way valves keep the blood from flowing backward. If the valves in a leg vein become damaged and a reverse flow occurs, the blood will pool, resulting in a varicose vein.

Our veins carry blood to the heart like rivers carry water to the sea, smaller tributaries merging into wider currents. Blood finally flows into the body's major veins, the venae cavae. One leads from the brain and chest, the other from the lower torso. These two great veins empty used blood into the right side of the heart, which immediately pumps the nearly toxic fluid into the lungs. Here the blood gets its fresh supply of oxygen and, now scarlet again, returns to the left side of the heart, ready for its life-giving journey around the body again—which you will recall takes only a minute; much less time than it takes to read about it.

THINKING IT OVER

(1) How long does it take a drop of blood to circulate around your body? _____

(2) What are the two loops of the double loop? _____

_____

_____

(3) What is the name of the body's largest artery? _____

STUDYING THE PASSAGE

(1) Find the Main Idea: Choose one.
  (a) Our cardiovascular system is like a river.
  (b) The cardiovascular system of our body.
  (c) How the cells receive oxygen.
  (d) The delicate balance of osmosis.   _____

(2) Find the Facts: Mark each one *true* or *false*.
 (a) Our blood goes on a sixty-thousand-mile journey.   _____
 (b) Our blood vessels are like rigid metal pipes.   _____
 (c) The artery wall is made up of six layers.   _____
 (d) The inner layer of the artery wall is smooth.   _____
 (e) There are billions of capillaries in the body.   _____
 (f) Arterioles pump blood into the capillaries.   _____
 (g) In one minute the water in blood plasma changes place with tissue liquids 45 times.   _____
 (h) The veins have more muscles than the arteries to get the blood back to the heart.   _____

(3) Find the Order: Number the following in the order in which they appear in the passage.
 (a) Fresh, oxygenated blood begins its voyage to the body's tissues.   _____
 (b) Bluish blood, laden with carbon dioxide and other wastes, flows sluggishly.   _____
 (c) The aorta's elastic membranes stretch with the impact of each surge of blood.   _____
 (d) One leads from the brain and chest, the other from the lower torso.   _____
 (e) As arteries divide and subdivide, the elastic membranes in their walls diminish.   _____
 (f) The powerful heart that propels this stream and the vessels that guide it are all alive.   _____
 (g) They replace waste and carbon dioxide with oxygen and nutrients, delivering life to the cell.   _____
 (h) Now the process of osmosis takes over.   _____

(4) Go beyond the Facts: The best way for a person to help the blood return to the heart is to:
 (a) Be sedentary—not moving around too much.
 (b) Be active—using the muscles of the body.
 (c) To keep to a regular routine, with plenty of sleep.
 (d) To eat a good diet.   _____

(5) Determine the Writer's Style and Technique: Which one of the following does the writer *not* do in giving her explanation?
 (a) Give facts and details.
 (b) Give the facts in a logical sequence.
 (c) Make a comparison.
 (d) Tell a humorous story.   _____

USING THE WORDS

(1) Words and Their Meanings: Find the boldfaced word for these definitions.

_____   (a) to make or become smaller

_____   (b) a fine cobweb or a thin thread from one; a very thin cloth

_____   (c) stopping and starting again from time to time

_____   (d) full of pores or tiny holes through which water, air, etc. may pass

_____   (e) rate of motion; speed

_____   (f) water removed from; dry

_____   (g) liquids passing through a thin membrane so as to become mixed and equal in strength on both sides

_____   (h) narrow bodies of water

(2) Write a paragraph using four of the words from the list above. Use a separate piece of paper.

WRITING ABOUT IT

Use a separate piece of paper.

(1) Underline, highlight, or make notes on the important facts and details in the passage. Then make a detailed outline of the passage, grouping the facts and details under appropriate headings. Include diagrams that might help you to better understand and remember the facts.

(2) The title of this passage is "The Powerful River." Write a story on a subject of your own choice which would appropriately have this title.

A LOVELY DAY—VALENTINE'S DAY

ABOUT THE PASSAGE   Valentine's Day is a day for lovers, and an opportunity to tell people you care about them. It is a truly lovely tradition that has been celebrated for a long time. Do you know its origin and who Valentine was?

REASON FOR READING   To read a historical account of a holiday and its customs.

READ THE PASSAGE

Every February 14, Americans exchange over 800 million valentines. And schoolchildren, using classroom drop boxes, send about 600 million. Whom do you think gets the most valentines? Teachers.

Americans are not the only ones with a tradition of sending cards or gifts to their sweethearts, family, or close friends. The English, French, Italians, and Danes, among others, do the same thing.

The holiday is named for a martyred priest named Valentine who was executed in A.D. 270 by the Romans for his religious activities. Old stories say that before his death, Valentine sent the blind daughter of his jailor a letter which he signed, "From your Valentine," and the phrase caught on. February 14 became Valentine's Day because the priest was later **canonized,** and February 14 was chosen as his feast day.

According to legend, however, the day goes back to the ancient Roman festival called the Feast of Lupercalia, which took place on February 15 to celebrate the arrival of spring and fertility. In addition to the purification and fertility rites performed, maidens fashioned love messages and deposited them in a large pot. These were drawn by the young men, who then courted the girls whose messages they had drawn.

When Christianity came to England, all the pagan celebrations and rituals were changed to have religious **connotations** and Christian names. Hence, it is believed the Feast of Lupercalia came to be known as St. Valentine's Day.

At any rate, the holiday came to be considered the appropriate date for choosing a sweetheart or announcing an engagement. There are many references to the custom of drawing one's valentine by lot. In Britain, the person whose name one drew became one's special partner for the whole year, often receiving expensive gifts. In many cases this matching led to an engagement. A French version of this custom required the girl to prepare a meal for her valentine, who contributed wine to **enhance** the food. They would end the evening at a public dance. Legend says that those who **rejected** their valentine were burned in **effigy** at a village bonfire.

Other Valentine's Day customs have also existed for a long time. They have ranged from the simple belief that it was bad luck for unmarried girls to bring snowdrops into the house that day, to the more **exotic** belief that if you snared an owl and two sparrows before sunrise you would acquire wisdom, humility, and good luck. Other bizarre superstitions along the same lines include sticking a rose leaf on your forehead in the belief that if it cracked, your valentine loved you; and boiling an egg, eating its white and shell, and going to bed without drinking or speaking so you would dream of your future mate.

The longest-surviving tradition, participated in by the most people, is sending cards or verses to one's valentine. There are British and French valentine poems dating from the 1400s. Writing valentines became an important art, particularly in the 1800s in Great Britain. There were even books published to supply the timid and unartistic with the widest choice of models suitable for every kind of person, such as *The Complete Valentine Writer, The Frolicsome Valentine Writer, The Gentleman's and Lady's Polite Valentine Writer*, and the *Quiver of Love.*

Around 1840 valentines became popular in America. By 1857 over three million valentines were sold, ranging in price from three cents to thirty dollars each. One person who was instrumental in boosting the American valentine market was Esther A. Howland of Worcester, Massachusetts. In 1848, when she was a young woman, Esther was kept at home because of a broken kneecap. In an effort to cheer her up, a business associate of her father's sent her a valentine card made in England. She liked the card very much and decided to make some of her own. Her brothers took some samples of her work on a business trip through other New England states. When they returned, they had five thousand dollars' worth of business. This created a career for Esther Howland overnight. For the next thirty years her work flourished.

Her business involved importing lace paper from England and paste-on decorations from Germany. Eventually she had her own **dies** made and produced her own paste-ons to save time. She invented two special ways of decorating valentines, both of which became popular and lasted for many years. She did not like **sentiments** on the front of the card so she kept them inside. Her earliest creations were predominantly white and beautifully simple.

The mass production of valentines began in the 1890s. With it the cards became coarser and lost the delicacy and vitality they had possessed during the 1850s. The commercialization of this day has continued in this century, but you can still find beautiful cards in shops today. Even though Valentine's Day is neither a business nor a school holiday in America, its popularity continues. It remains a day close to the heart of many Americans.

THINKING IT OVER

(1) Who was Valentine? _____

(2) How far back in history is there evidence that cards or verses were sent to valentines? _____

(3) Who made the first commercial valentine cards in America? _____

When was this? _____

STUDYING THE PASSAGE

(1) Find the Main Idea: Choose one.
   (a) Valentine's Day is for sweethearts.
   (b) What to do on Valentine's Day.
   (c) Why valentines are written.
   (d) The origins and customs of Valentine's Day.   _____

(2) Find the Facts: Mark each one *true* or *false*.
   (a) In America, approximately 14 million valentine cards are exchanged on Valentine's Day.   _____
   (b) Valentine lived in ancient Roman times.   _____
   (c) The Feast of Lupercalia was an ancient British celebration.   _____
   (d) British girls and boys drew the name of their valentine by lot.   _____
   (e) Taking snowdrops into the house supposedly brought bad luck for unmarried girls.   _____
   (f) Writing valentines became an art form.   _____
   (g) Valentines became popular in America around the 1880s.   _____
   (h) Mass production of valentine cards began in the 1890s.   _____

(3) Find the Order: Number the following in the order in which they appear in the passage.
   (a) Other Valentine's Day customs have also existed for a long time.   _____
   (b) These were drawn by the young men, who then courted the girls.   _____

(c) It remains a day close to the heart of many Americans.   _____

(d) Americans are not the only ones with a tradition of sending cards.   _____

(e) They had five thousand dollars' worth of business.   _____

(f) There were books published to supply the timid and unartistic with the widest choice
of models.   _____

(g) Pagan celebrations and rituals were changed.   _____

(h) Valentine sent the blind daughter of his jailor a letter.   _____

(4) Go beyond the Facts: Which one of the following could you *not* conclude from the passage?

    (a) Valentine's Day has its roots in the acknowledgment of spring, fertility, and the
perpetuation of life's cycle.

    (b) Valentine's Day has been celebrated for many years in some form or other.

    (c) Superstition seems to be closely associated with Valentine's Day.

    (d) Valentine's Day is less popular today than it used to be.   _____

(5) Determine the Writer's Style and Technique: Which one does the writer *not* do?

    (a) Present facts.

    (b) Give examples.

    (c) Give an opinion.

    (d) Relate stories.   _____

USING THE WORDS

(1) Words and Their Meanings: Find the boldfaced word for these definitions.

_____ (a) suggesting an idea or feeling in addition to the actual meaning

_____ (b) made a saint

_____ (c) strange, different, foreign

_____ (d) refused to take

_____ (e) tools used to cut or press a shape into paper, fabric, etc.

_____ (f) feelings, especially tender feelings

_____ (g) a statue or other image of a person; a crude figure of a person who
is hated

_____ (h) to make better

(2) Write a paragraph using four of the words from the list above. Use a separate piece of paper.

WRITING ABOUT IT

Use a separate piece of paper.

(1) Reread the passage if you think you need to. Then, without referring to the passage, describe the origins
and customs associated with Valentine's Day.

(2) Be prepared for next Valentine's Day. Write a letter or a poem to someone you care about very much.

THE AMERICAN MOTHER

ABOUT THE PASSAGE   There is no greater American than the American mother. How she accomplishes all that she does never ceases to amaze her fellow Americans. It is no wonder we devote a special day in our calendar to honor her.

REASON FOR READING   To learn how Mother's Day came about.

READ THE PASSAGE

The role of the American mother in our history has always been remarkable. Today, she continues to impress and surprise us as she assumes key positions in government, politics, and business. She is no longer expected to always stay at home to do the housework, look after the kids, and prepare the meals. Now, she does all that and, at the same time, is a Supreme Court Justice, a Governor of a state, a member of the Cabinet, or a CEO of some of the biggest corporations in America. She is a truck driver, an auto mechanic, or an electrical engineer. She serves in the armed forces, now in combat. She is a lawyer, a doctor, a teacher, or an architect.

It is not surprising that we have a special day to honor mothers. That day has become one of the most **revered** of our special days. Card manufacturers and stores report that their clients and sales increase at that time of year. For many restaurateurs it is their busiest day of the year, surpassing Christmas, Hanukkah, and New Year's.

Contrary to many beliefs, Mother's Day did not originate in America, nor was it developed by merchandisers purely as a commercial enterprise. The tradition began in England in the late 1400s when young people were given a special holiday from their **apprenticeship** to return to their home town and churches to observe a mid-**Lenten** Sunday. Then it was called "Mothering Sunday" and the apprentices would take gifts for their mothers. They often brought a special English **delicacy** called simnel cake. This custom is mentioned in an old English poem*:

"I'll to thee a Simnel bring
" 'Gainst thou go'st a-mothering;
So that when she blesseth thee,
Half that blessing thou'lt give me."

Mother's Day in England is still observed in mid-Lent, on the fourth Sunday in Lent (about twenty weekdays before Easter). In some other European countries it comes on Saint Anne's Day, which is on July 26, and commemorates the mother of the Virgin Mary.

Mother's Day was first suggested as an American celebration in 1872 by Julia Ward Howe, who wrote the famous "Battle Hymn of the Republic" of the Civil War. She wanted Independence Day to be Mother's Day and a day of peace. But nothing came of her idea.

However, in 1907 a Pennsylvania woman named Anna Jarvis decided to establish a special day for mothers in memory of her mother. She started a nationwide campaign, traveling all over the country, giving speeches, and rallying people to her cause. By 1913 practically every state had set aside a special day to honor mothers. In May 1914, President Wilson gave the day official national recognition. He signed a **joint resolution** of Congress directing officials to display the American flag as "a public expression of our love and reverence for the mothers of our country." The resolution also stated that the day would always fall on the second Sunday in May.

Some say that the custom of wearing a white carnation on Mother's Day originated because President Wilson wore one on the first official Mother's Day. However, it was actually chosen by Anna Jarvis, because her mother had a great love for flowers. She chose a white carnation because, as Ann Hark says in an article:

"The whiteness of the blossom . . . represents the purity of motherhood; the **calyx** symbolizes life; its fragrance is like the **incense** of a mother's prayers; its

* *Hesperides*, by Robert Herrick.

wide field of growth **exemplifies** the boundless charity of a mother's love; its enduring characteristics, her fidelity. And, crowning touch of all, the carnation's habit of folding its faded petals to its heart instead of dropping . . . illustrates as no other picture could, the undying quality of a mother's love."*

Anna Jarvis had the deep satisfaction of seeing her dream come true. However, as Mother's Day grew in popularity, it became more commercialized.

Greeting card and telephone companies, florists, candy stores, and restaurants all took advantage of the day, urging people to remember their mothers. This distressed Anna Jarvis very much and she made great efforts to prevent it, to little avail.

Whether Mother's Day has become too commercialized or not, the attention we give to this day shows the great respect, admiration, and love Americans have for their mom.

THINKING IT OVER

(1) (a) In which country did Mother's Day originate? _____

    (b) When was this? _____

    (c) What was the reason for this holiday? _____

_____

(2) When is the American Mother's Day? _____

(3) Who started Mother's Day in America? _____

STUDYING THE PASSAGE

(1) Find the Main Idea: Choose one.
    (a) How Mother's Day was established in America.
    (b) Why we revere our mothers in America.
    (c) The commercialization of Mother's Day.
    (d) The history of the day we commemorate our mothers.   ____

(2) Find the Facts: Mark each one *true* or *false*.
    (a) There seems to be no job our mothers can't do.   ____
    (b) Some restaurateurs say Mother's Day is their busiest day of the year.   ____
    (c) Mother's Day in England was always on a Sunday.   ____
    (d) Anna Jarvis was the first person to suggest a Mother's Day in America.   ____
    (e) Mother's Day became a nationally acknowledged day in 1924.   ____
    (f) A rose became a symbol of Mother's Day.   ____
    (g) The whiteness of the blossom represents the purity of motherhood.   ____
    (h) Anna Jarvis was distressed that Mother's Day was becoming commercialized.   ____

(3) Find the Order: Number the following in the order in which they appear in the passage.
    (a) President Wilson wore one on the first official Mother's Day.   ____
    (b) Today, she continues to impress and surprise us.   ____
    (c) Its fragrance is like the incense of a mother's prayers.   ____
    (d) In some other European countries it comes on Saint Anne's Day.   ____
    (e) Whether Mother's Day has become too commercialized or not . . .   ____
    (f) She started a nationwide campaign.   ____

* From "The Mother of Mother's Day" by Ann Hark in *The Country Gentleman*, © 1956. Used with permission from the Curtis Publishing Company.

(g) It is not surprising we have a special day to honor her. _____

(h) Then it was called "Mothering Sunday." _____

(4) Go beyond the Facts: From reading the passage you could conclude which one of the following:

(a) Mothers like the attention paid to them on Mother's Day.

(b) Children use Mother's Day to make up for all the problems they have caused their mothers during the year.

(c) One person can make an impact.

(d) It takes many people to bring about a national day. _____

(5) Determine the Writer's Style and Technique: Which one of the following does the writer use to tell you about Mother's Day?

(a) Question and answer.

(b) Straightforward presentation of the facts.

(c) Personal comments.

(d) Anecdotes. _____

USING THE WORDS

(1) Words and Their Meanings: Find the boldfaced word for these definitions.

_____ (a) related to the forty weekdays before Easter, a time of fasting and repenting in Christian churches

_____ (b) agreed to by both the House and Senate

_____ (c) shows by giving or being an example of

_____ (d) loved and respected greatly

_____ (e) learning a trade by helping a person skilled in that trade

_____ (f) a substance made of gum and spices that is burned for the sweet smell it gives off; a sweet smell

_____ (g) a special, choice food

_____ (h) the outer ring of leaves, or sepals, growing at the base of a flower

(2) Write a paragraph using four of the words from the list above. Use a separate piece of paper.

WRITING ABOUT IT

Use a separate piece of paper.

(1) Describe your mother or someone who has been significant in your life. Give a complete picture of her or him: what she or he looks like; how this person moves, acts, and speaks; her or his personality, likes and dislikes; what she or he does at work and in her or his free time; her or his beliefs, religion, and philosophy of life; and her or his relationship with you.

(2) Write a letter to your mother or someone who has been significant in your life—which she or he need not see—expressing your feelings for her or him. Mention the things she or he has given you that you are grateful for; and tell this person about the things you have accomplished that you think would make her or him proud of you.

THE HOLOCAUST*

ABOUT THE PASSAGE

How we humans could be so brutal to one another is the question we should ask ourselves when we talk or read about the Holocaust. It is a page in our history that we can never forget.

REASON FOR READING

As you read about the systematic elimination of the Jews and other groups, notice how the introduction of specific examples and statistics gives greater impact to the account.

READ THE PASSAGE

Their businesses were **boycotted** and their jobs were taken from them. They were dragged from their homes and hunted in the fields. They were herded into gas chambers and burned in ovens. They were gunned down on city streets and hanged, and they were shot in forests and dumped in communal graves.

Who were these people? Jews were the primary victims—six million of them. But they also included Gypsies, the handicapped, homosexuals, Jehovah's Witnesses, Poles, and Soviet prisoners of war—those who were considered a threat to the purity of the German race, or "master race," as they called themselves.

The Holocaust was the state-sponsored, systematic persecution and **annihilation** of European Jews and other groups by Nazi Germany and its collaborators between 1933 and 1945.

The events of the Holocaust occurred in two main phases: 1933–1939 and 1939–1945.

1933–1939

On January 30, 1933, Adolf Hitler was named Chancellor, the most powerful position in the German government. Once in power, Hitler moved quickly to end German democracy. He convinced his cabinet to **invoke** emergency clauses of the Constitution that permitted suspension of individual freedoms of press, speech, and assembly. Special security forces—the Special State Police (the Ge-

stapo), the Storm Troopers (SA) and the Security Police (SS)—murdered or arrested leaders of the opposition political parties. The Enabling Act of March 23, 1933 gave Hitler dictatorial powers.

In 1933, the Nazis began to put their racial ideology into practice. Jews, who numbered 600,000 in Germany (less than one percent of the total population), became the principal target. New laws forced Jews to leave government, university, and other public jobs. Laws created in 1935 made Jews second-class citizens. These "Nuremberg" laws defined Jews, not by their religion or by how they wanted to identify themselves, but by the religious **affiliation** of their grandparents.

Between 1937 and 1939, anti-Jewish regulations segregated Jews further, making life very difficult: they could not attend public schools, go to theaters, movies, or vacation resorts, or reside—or even walk—in certain sections of the cities. During this period, Jews were also forced out of Germany's economic life. The Nazis either seized Jewish businesses and properties outright or forced Jews to sell them at artificially low prices. In November 1938, this economic attack changed into the physical destruction of synagogues and Jewish homes and stores. Then came the systematic roundup of Jews and their deportation to concentration camps.

At the same time the Nazis acted against the other groups whom they felt were racially or **genet-**

---

*This selection was developed from information and materials provided by the U.S. Holocaust Memorial Museum. Used by courtesy of the U.S. Holocaust Memorial Museum, Washington, D.C.

ically "inferior," and against anyone who tried to help the persecuted people. Thousands were imprisoned in concentration camps.

1939–1945

On September 1, 1939, Germany invaded Poland and World War II began. Within days, the Polish army was defeated and the Nazis began their campaign to destroy Polish culture and enslave the Polish people, whom they considered subhuman. Large segments of the population were resettled or put into concentration camps to create new living space for the "superior Germanic race."

Approximately 3 million Polish Jews were forced into 400 sealed **ghettos** where starvation, overcrowding, exposure to cold, and contagious diseases killed tens of thousands of them.

At the same time Hitler ordered all handicapped persons deemed "incurable" to be killed, since they could not contribute to society and weakened the race.

After the Germans defeated Denmark, Norway, the Netherlands, Belgium, Luxembourg, and France, and invaded the Soviet Union, they set up ghettos and forced labor camps as well as concentration camps. There were many mass executions; the overwhelming majority of those killed were Jews. In the Soviet Union, for example, the murders were carried out by mobile killing squads who followed in the wake of the invading German army. The most famous of these sites was Babi Yar, near Kiev, where an estimated 33,000 were murdered.

Between 1942 and 1944, the Germans moved to eliminate the ghettos in occupied Poland and elsewhere. They deported the residents to "extermination camps"—killing centers equipped with gassing facilities—located in Poland. In late January, 1942,

the decision to implement the "final solution of the Jewish question" became formal state policy, and Jews from western Europe were also sent to the killing centers.

To understand the enormity and horror of these purges, one has only to look at the statistics. In Treblinka Center alone, at least 750,000 were killed. At Belzec more than 600,000 persons were killed between May 1942 and August 1943. More than 1.25 million people were killed at Auschwitz-Birkenau.

The methods of murder were the same in all the killing centers, which were operated by the SS. The victims arrived in railroad freight cars and passenger trains. On arrival, men were separated from women and children. Prisoners were forced to undress and hand over all valuables. They were then driven naked into the gas chambers, which were disguised as shower rooms, and either carbon monoxide or zyklon B (a form of crystalline prussic acid) was used to **asphyxiate** them. The minority selected for forced labor were, after initial quarantine, **vulnerable** to malnutrition, exposure, epidemics, brutality, and even medical experiments. Many perished as a result.

In May 1945, Nazi Germany collapsed. The Allies liberated the remaining interns of the camps and the nightmare began to end.

What is disturbing about the Holocaust is that it was not only the elite SS who carried out the systematic, murderous activities. Documentary evidence indicates that *ordinary* Germany police and army units were very much involved, as well as local collaborators in many of the overrun countries. One must also note the **acquiescence** or indifference of millions of bystanders.

What does this say about human beings? It is a question we should all ponder.

THINKING IT OVER

(1) The Jews were the main target of Nazi Germany, but other groups were also purged. Give five of these

groups: _____

_____

(2) How many Jews died in the Holocaust? _____

STUDYING THE PASSAGE

(1) Find the Main Idea: Choose one.
  (a) How the Jews were killed by Nazi Germany.
  (b) The systematic persecution of groups who threatened Germany's purity.
  (c) The effect of the Holocaust upon mankind.
  (d) The suffering Nazi Germany caused. _____

(2) Find the Facts: Mark each one *true* or *false*.
  (a) The Jews were always killed in gas chambers. _____
  (b) Once in power Hitler quickly brought an end to German democracy. _____
  (c) The Enabling Act of 1933 was an attempt to curb Hitler's powers. _____
  (d) The "Nuremberg" laws defined Jews by the religious affiliation of their grandparents. _____
  (e) The Nazis created new laws to make life intolerable for the Jews. _____
  (f) The Polish Jews were isolated from their fellow citizens. _____
  (g) 1.25 million people were killed at Auschwitz-Birkenau. _____
  (h) Those who were not sent to the gas chambers were the lucky ones who survived. _____

(3) Find the Order: Number the following in the order in which they appear in the passage.
  (a) On September 1, 1939, Germany invaded Poland and World War II began. _____
  (b) The Allies liberated interns of the camps. _____
  (c) Prisoners were forced to undress and hand over all valuables. _____
  (d) They were dragged from their homes and hunted in the fields. _____
  (e) The murders were carried out by mobile killing squads who followed in the wake of the invading German army. _____
  (f) He convinced his cabinet to invoke emergency clauses of the Constitution. _____
  (g) They could not attend public schools. _____
  (h) To understand the enormity and horror of these purges, one has only to look at the statistics. _____

(4) Go beyond the Facts: In this selection, the writer indicates that:
  (a) The Holocaust was the result of a select group who felt the German race was superior.
  (b) Ordinary citizens played a part in the Holocaust.
  (c) All the blame for the Holocaust should be placed on Hitler.
  (d) The Holocaust was the result of many different factors, such as the German economy and jealousy of the Jews' accomplishments. _____

(5) Determine the Writer's Style and Technique: Which *one* of the following best describes the writer's account of the Holocaust?
  (a) It is an emotional account.
  (b) It is an objective, factual account.
  (c) It sides with the Jews and other purged groups.
  (d) It gives reasons for the Nazis' behavior. _____

USING THE WORDS

(1) Words and Their Meanings: Find the boldfaced word for these definitions.

_____ (a) to call for aid or protection; to ask for in a serious way

_____ (b) a section of a city in which a particular group of people live or are forced to live

_____ (c) to join together in refusing to buy, sell, or use something, or to have any dealings with someone

_____ (d) agreement without argument

_____ (e) membership, or part (of a group)

_____ (f) to make unconscious by cutting down the supply of oxygen in the blood

_____ (g) complete destruction

_____ (h) having to do with genes or heredity

_____ (i) able to be hurt, destroyed, attacked

(2) Write a paragraph using four of the words from the list above. Use a separate piece of paper.

WRITING ABOUT IT

Use a separate piece of paper.

(1) Research the Holocaust. If possible, read a variety of books and materials: factual, historical accounts; personal accounts; memoirs and diaries; as well as fiction, poetry, and books of art that the interns created. Then write your own account of the Holocaust, using any format or approach you wish.*

(2) Imagine you are a Jew in Nazi Germany. Write an entry in your diary telling how you are managing to escape from being captured. Include in your description: your hiding place; what you do during the day and night; the people you rely on for help; your thoughts and feelings; and your hopes for the future.

* For a comprehensive list of books and materials on the Holocaust, write to the United States Holocaust Memorial Museum, 100 Raoul Wallenberg Place, S.W., Washington, D.C. 20024-2150. Internet address: www.ushmm.org

FIRSTS IN HEART OPERATIONS

ABOUT THE PASSAGE

Complete heart transplants became a reality in 1967, but when do you think the first heart surgery was performed?

    (a) In 1951
    (b) In 1926
    (c) In 1893
    (d) In 1872

Who performed the first heart transplant?

    (a) An American
    (b) A South African
    (c) A Canadian
    (d) A Japanese

REASON FOR READING

To notice the order in which the writer presents the facts, and to discover which section presents events in chronological sequence and which employs a different method of organization.

READ THE PASSAGE

James Cornish lay in the hospital emergency room, blood gushing from a stab wound in his chest. He had been in a fierce street brawl and a knife had penetrated his heart.

The doctor bent over the burly man. Emergency treatment had not stopped the bleeding, so he decided to operate. Dr. Williams first cut open the chest cavity and then the wall surrounding the stabbed heart. As the other doctors held the cavity open, he checked to see if the heart was still beating. Miraculously, it was.

Carefully and skillfully he sewed up the wound. The heart faltered and then continued to beat. The man would live!

Why was this such an unusual operation? Because the year was 1893. At that time anyone with a heart wound was given sedatives and a prayer, and invariably died. There were no X-ray machines, no heart-lung machines, no miracle drugs, and no blood banks for transfusions. These medical tools were still unknown.

Who was this Dr. Williams? He was a black member of the staff of Providence Hospital, which he helped to establish when he found that blacks were not allowed to use the hospital facilities in Chicago. Providence not only trained blacks as doctors and nurses, but also served the black community, bringing an end to such operations as kitchen-table tonsillectomies in Chicago.

Daniel Hale Williams had struggled to achieve all that he did. His father died when he was twelve. The family was so poor that the only schoolbook they could buy him was a dictionary. After graduation from high school, he took a job in the Surgeon General's office. Within two years he had learned so much about medicine that he was admitted directly to medical school without having gone to college. He was a brilliant student, and upon graduation was asked to remain at the school to teach anatomy and surgery. But in response to the black people of Chicago, Dr. Williams joined the staff at Providence. It was in this hospital that he rose from unsung neighborhood hero to one of America's greatest surgeons.

Many years later, miles away in another country, another doctor was preparing to play a part in the pioneering of surgery. This doctor had many more advantages than Dr. Williams, but he was no less dedicated to his profession and to the task he had set himself: to improve heart surgery. Dr. Christiaan Barnard had trained at Cape Town University in South Africa and had continued researching and experimenting with animals while carrying on his **practice.** He had also visited numerous countries in order to learn about the most advanced medical techniques. He paid visits to the United States, attended conferences and seminars, and visited medical centers in Europe, the former Soviet Union, India, Australia, and New Zealand.

Finally the time came when Dr. Barnard felt that he had acquired the necessary techniques to perform the operation no one had attempted before: a heart transplant. He had an ideal patient, a large, former amateur boxer named Louis Washkansky, who had been clinging to life for two and a half years, although all doctors had given up his case as hopeless. No existing remedy could save him; he suffered from **gross** heart failure. His heart had become so big that it was only one inch from the left border of the chest and two inches from the right. In fact, his heart was two-thirds dead. How he continued to live astonished even the physicians of the cardiac clinic. Yet this man continued to carry on his wholesale grocery business, showing how a strong will can bring about a miracle.

However, when Dr. Barnard learned of this courageous man, his strength was rapidly beginning to wane. When doctors suggested to Washkansky that he be the first man to receive a new heart, he agreed without hesitation. He knew he was near death and that this was his only chance of survival. He was put into the hospital to await the operation, but day after day dragged on. Everyone was ready, but there was no heart to transplant.

Then one day a young woman was crossing the street with her mother to take a cake she had just bought to her father and brother waiting nearby. Suddenly there was a thud, a bang, a loud screech of tires. Denise Darvall and her mother had been struck by a car. Mrs. Darvall was dead and Denise was virtually dead. She had multiple cuts and broken bones, and her brain had been severely damaged.

Denise was taken immediately to the hospital, where doctors did all that they could. But they knew it was hopeless. They managed to keep the vital organs working, but her brain had ceased to function. Denise had entered a no-man's land between life and death—an area created by modern science and medicine. She was being held there by stimulants, blood transfusions, and, most important, artificial breathing provided by an automatic respirator. How long it would take her to cross over to total death depended on how long the doctors continued to run the machine. When it stopped, her heart would stop beating within three to five minutes. At that point the three criteria that doctors have used for centuries to determine death would prevail: no heartbeat, no respiration, no brain function. Then Denise, who was already medically dead, would be legally dead.

While Denise's organs were kept alive artificially it was possible for her heart to be removed and used, but as soon as her heart stopped beating, it would begin to deteriorate. And so, with her father's permission, she was brought to the operating theater next to the theater where Louis Washkansky waited. The operations that were about to occur raised all sorts of questions. What right do we have to take the last gleam of existence? Even though someone is considered medically dead, should we not still keep the organs going if we have a chance? And yet, what right do we have to condemn people to **insentient** existences where they are unable to see, to speak, or to feel the world around them? Even worse, suppose one small, conscious area of the brain lived on undetected, so that the individual suffered pain or was in some way **mutely** aware of the indignities heaped upon the body, enduring the tangle of rubber hoses, tubes, and needles necessary to sustain life.

These and many other thoughts filled Dr. Christiaan Barnard's mind as he walked alone down the passage to the operating theaters that day in December 1967. He hesitated as doubt began to grow within him. Was he doing the right thing? Was this the right time for such an operation? With each step he took, the weight of doubt grew. He suddenly wanted to turn back, but he knew he could not. Two people—a young woman and a man—were being moved into the adjacent theaters. Both of them had living hearts that could not continue to beat much longer; he could give life to one of them. If he succeeded, it would be more than the grafting of a heart. It would be not only the crowning effort of a skilled team of men and women, but also a **conjoining** of the many **disciplines** of medicine and science. It would bring a new era and a new hope for all people.

Many heart transplants have been performed since then, but it was Christiaan Barnard's courage, as well as his superb knowledge and technical ability, that made the later ones possible. Like Dr. Daniel Hale Williams before him, he had done the seemingly impossible. But unlike Dr. Williams' operation, the one Dr. Barnard performed raised many issues that go far beyond the medical world; now we are faced with a **moral** and ethical question: Are we **meddling** with life itself?

THINKING IT OVER

(1) When was the first heart surgery performed? _____

(2) (a) Who performed the first heart transplant? _____

   (b) What nationality was he? _____

(3) Whose heart was used for the first heart transplant? _____

_____

(4) Who was the first recipient of a heart transplant? _____

_____

STUDYING THE PASSAGE

(1) Find the Main Idea: Choose one.
   (a) Two doctors, through hard work and courage, have contributed to the knowledge and techniques of heart surgery.
   (b) Doctors are still making new discoveries to increase our life span.
   (c) Williams performed the first open-heart surgery in the United States.
   (d) Heart transplants are immoral and unethical. _____

(2) Find the Facts: Mark each one *true* or *false*.
   (a) The first heart operation was in 1893. _____
   (b) Daniel Hale Williams was a white doctor dedicated to helping black people. _____
   (c) Dr. Williams was admitted to medical school although he had never gone to college. _____
   (d) Dr. Barnard was a native of Australia. _____
   (e) Dr. Barnard prepared himself by visiting many countries and learning new techniques before he performed the first heart transplant. _____
   (f) Denise was dead on arrival at the hospital. _____
   (g) Barnard worried about the moral and ethical questions as well as the medical problems connected with the operation. _____
   (h) The right timing was crucial to the transferral of the heart. _____

(3) Find the Order: Number the following in the order in which they appear in the passage.
   (a) At that point the three criteria that doctors have used for centuries to determine death would prevail. _____
   (b) There were no X-ray machines, no heart-lung machines, no miracle drugs. _____
   (c) He hesitated as doubt began to grow within him. _____
   (d) He was a large, former amateur boxer. _____

(e) The family was so poor that they could only buy him one schoolbook.   ____

(f) Emergency treatment had not stopped the bleeding, so he decided to operate.   ____

(g) He was put into the hospital to await the operation.   ____

(h) He paid visits to the United States.   ____

(4) Go beyond the Facts: Which one is *not* true?

  (a) Research from many countries contributed to Dr. Barnard's successful operation.

  (b) Heart transplant operations raise many moral and ethical questions.

  (c) A heart can continue to beat while a person is medically dead.

  (d) A heart can only be transferred from one human to another when they are
      physically alike.   ____

(5) Determine the Writer's Style and Technique: The author (choose more than one):

  (a) Reports only the facts and avoids making direct comments.

  (b) Creates a sense of excitement and suspense by holding back the outcome
      as you follow events step by step.

  (c) Creates excitement by describing a vivid action scene.

  (d) Gives many details.   ____ ____

USING THE WORDS

(1) Words and Their Meanings: Find the boldfaced word for these definitions.

  _____   (a) unconscious, inanimate

  _____   (b) total, entire; obvious, flagrant

  _____   (c) the exercise of a profession

  _____   (d) silently, speechlessly

  _____   (e) interfering

  _____   (f) putting together, linking

  _____   (g) concerned with right and wrong behavior

  _____   (h) subject areas, fields of study

(2) Write a paragraph using four of the words from the list above. Use a separate piece of paper.

WRITING ABOUT IT

Use a separate piece of paper.

(1) As the passage mentions, transplant operations have raised many different questions and issues. Discuss them and give your opinion whether transplant operations should be allowed.

(2) Louis Washkansky was given a new chance for life. Imagine you were given the opportunity to lead a completely *new* life. Describe where you would live, the lifestyle you would have, and how different it would be from your present life.

A RUNNER WHO COULD NOT WALK

ABOUT THE PASSAGE Naming the greatest runner who ever lived would be very difficult, but the runner described in this passage must be the most unusual one. He broke the world's indoor mile record. Do you know who he is and what made him so unusual? What does his story teach us?

REASON FOR READING Practice your speed reading. Read the passage as fast as you can, noticing how the writer wins our sympathy for the person she is describing. Immediately answer the questions, then check your answers by rereading the passage.

READ THE PASSAGE

When he was seven, Glenn Cunningham was a healthy boy who admired his older brother Floyd for his great running ability. Every morning Glenn and Floyd ran three miles to school to **stoke** the school-house furnace. But one day a catastrophe occurred. The furnace exploded in their faces. Glenn was thrown from the building by the blast. He searched for Floyd outside the building, only to learn that he was still inside the school. Glenn ran back into the fire to save his brother, but flames surged toward him. The smoke was **suffocating.** Glenn yelled, "Floyd! Floyd! Answer me!" as he fought his way toward the furnace. Then he fell unconscious. He could not save Floyd.

Glenn awoke in his bed, his body oiled and bound in bandages. He tried to get up, but the **excruciating** pain in his legs made him **wince** and sob. His right leg was crooked and pulled up at the knee. Almost all his left foot was burned and could not bear his weight. The doctors said Glenn would never run again.

Weeks later the bandages were removed and Glenn was given crutches. He was almost eleven years old before he discarded them, and he was almost thirteen before the stiffness left his right leg and it became straight again.

He and his family rubbed and stretched his legs every morning and every evening. When his family tired, he would lie awake and rub his own legs. In time it became less painful to run than to walk; he was gradually overcoming his **handicap.**

At fourteen, Glenn began running wherever he went. The rubbing and the running must have done the trick, because at sixteen he made the high school track team.

At first, Glenn decided to become a **sprinter,** and he achieved speeds few long-distance runners could produce. He ran his first quarter-mile in 58.5 seconds, his second in 64.0, his third in 61.7, and his final in 60.2.

However, one day he ran the whole mile, and to everyone's surprise he set a record of four minutes, thirty seconds. He continued training while at Dartmouth College in Hanover, New Hampshire. On March 3, 1938, at Dartmouth's huge indoor track, he ran the mile in a world record time of four minutes, 4.4 seconds. The track was 261½ yards a lap (approximately six and two-thirds laps to the mile) and made of spruce boards laid on a bed of cinders. It was considered one of the world's fastest indoor ovals, but Cunningham's determination, courage, and years of perseverance and training were responsible for his victory.

Cunningham brought honor to his country by winning a silver medal at the Berlin Olympics in 1936, and it is generally believed that had it not been for the Second World War, he might have been **immortalized** as history's first four-minute miler.

Ever since the **genesis** of modern athletics, the mile has been one of the most glamorous events of track and field. The mile has also given rise to some of the most exciting races and some of the most outstanding personalities: there was the Olympic victory of Jack Lovelock in 1936; the classic race between John Landy and Roger Bannister in the Commonwealth Games at Vancouver, Canada; the surprise victory of Josy Barthel in the Helsinki Olympics; and the fantastic consistency of Herb Elliott at his peak. But over the years, very few athletes achieved success by overcoming such difficulties as those that faced Glenn Cunningham, the man who was told he would never run again.

THINKING IT OVER

(1) Name three of Glenn Cunningham's athletic achievements. _____

_____

_____

(2) What was probably Glenn Cunningham's greatest feat? _____

_____

STUDYING THE PASSAGE

(1) Find the Main Idea: Choose one.
  (a) Glenn Cunningham broke the world record for the mile.
  (b) Glenn Cunningham tried to save his brother from the fire.
  (c) Glenn Cunningham learned to run again.
  (d) Glenn Cunningham was a fine person. _____

(2) Find the Facts: Mark each one *true* or *false*.
  (a) Glenn admired Floyd for his running ability. _____
  (b) Glenn was trapped inside the schoolhouse when the furnace exploded. _____
  (c) Glenn's left leg was crooked and bent backward. _____
  (d) Every day Glenn and his family rubbed and stretched his legs. _____
  (e) It was more painful for him to walk than to run. _____
  (f) At first Glenn tried to be a pole vaulter. _____
  (g) Glenn held the world record for the mile while he was in college. _____
  (h) Glenn won a gold medal at the Olympics. _____

(3) Find the Order: Number the following in the order in which they appear in the passage.
  (a) Glenn ran the mile in four minutes, 4.4 seconds. _____
  (b) At seven, Glenn was a healthy boy. _____
  (c) At sixteen, Glenn made the track team. _____
  (d) The furnace exploded in their faces. _____
  (e) At eleven, Glenn discarded the crutches. _____
  (f) Glenn's body was badly burned by the fire. _____
  (g) Glenn was given crutches. _____
  (h) Floyd died in the fire. _____

(4) Go beyond the Facts: It seems most correct to conclude from the selection that (choose two):
  (a) Glenn Cunningham was determined to be a greater runner than Floyd.
  (b) Glenn Cunningham possessed unusual courage.
  (c) Glenn Cunningham overcame an obstacle to achieve his goal.
  (d) Glenn Cunningham wasn't as badly burned as the doctors thought. _____ _____

(5) Determine the Writer's Style and Technique: Choose one. The author
    (a) Uses facts to show cause and effect.
    (b) Gives examples to show what something is.
    (c) Tells a story that illustrates a point.
    (d) Compares and contrasts to define something.   _____

USING THE WORDS

(1) Words and Their Meanings: Find the boldfaced word for these definitions.

    _____   (a) given fame that lasts even after death

    _____   (b) to supply with fuel

    _____   (c) choking, deprived of air, stifling

    _____   (d) to flinch or give an involuntary start, as in pain or distress

    _____   (e) physical or mental disability that may prevent normal achievement; disadvantage

    _____   (f) intense or extreme

    _____   (g) one who runs at top speed for a short distance

    _____   (h) origin, birth

(2) Write a paragraph using four of the words from the list above. Use a separate piece of paper.

WRITING ABOUT IT

Use a separate piece of paper.

(1) Find out about an athlete you admire, or who has an interesting story like Glenn Cunningham. Write your athlete's story, describing his or her background and achievements, and how the athlete achieved success.

(2) Write a story that begins: "He awoke in bed, his body oiled and bound in bandages. He tried to get up, but the terrible pain in his legs made him wince and sob." Make your story different from the one here. You can write about a girl or woman if you wish.

WHAT IS THE BIGGEST IN OUR SOLAR SYSTEM?

ABOUT THE PASSAGE

The sun is the biggest object in our solar system and vital to our survival. It is the central fire upon which all life on Earth depends. Less than a hundred years ago we knew little about it. However, now that we understand the principles of nuclear fusion, we not only know what processes go on in the sun, but we can even duplicate them.

REASON FOR READING

This is a difficult, technical explanation. Read it slowly and carefully, and study the diagrams. Note the headings in italics and underline, highlight, or make notes on the important facts. After you have read each part, see if you can answer the questions in the heading. If you can't, go back over it before going on to the next part.

READ THE PASSAGE

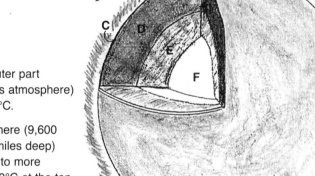

A Corona (outer part of the Sun's atmosphere) —2 million°C.

B Chromosphere (9,600 km/6,000 miles deep) —4,000°C to more than 50,000°C at the top.

C Photosphere (400 km/249 miles deep) —6,000°C.

D Convective zone (where gases move around).

E Radiative zone.

F Solar interior— 15 million°C. Nuclear reactions take place here.

The sun is a star, one of 100,000 million stars in our galaxy, the Milky Way. Although it is a very ordinary star in the galaxy, it is the center of our solar system. Not only is it the largest object in our solar system, it is crucial to our existence.

The sun is the engine of our life. By the radiation of its electromagnetic energy, the sun furnishes directly or indirectly all of the energy supporting life on Earth, because all foods and fuels are derived ultimately from plants using the energy of sunlight.

One second of the energy given off by the sun is 13 million times greater than the average amount of electricity used each year in the United States. Or, to put it another way: In one second the sun gives off more energy than all people have produced during their entire stay on Earth.

It is hard to believe that one star can produce such a large amount of energy, but it can. Yet our planet receives only about two-billionths of the total energy output of the sun. The rest streams out in all directions into space. On the average, each square meter (1.196 sq. yards) of the earth's surface receives enough solar energy to heat and light one small room. If only we knew how to capture more of that energy!

How does the sun generate this energy? The total amount of energy given off by the sun is almost constant, varying by no more than a few tenths of 1 percent over several days. This energy output is generated deep within the sun, at its core. Here, hydrogen atoms are fused into helium at a temperature of 27 million°F (15 million°C). If a pinhead were this hot, it would catch on fire and destroy everything for 60 miles (100 km) around it. Energy, in the form of violent gamma rays, is released.

The energy is transported most of the way to the sun's surface, which is 300,000 miles above the core, by radiation. Nearer the surface, however, in the **convection zone,** energy is transported by currents of rising and sinking gas. This action is similar to that in a pot of boiling water, in which gas bubbles carry energy to the surface of the water. The turbulence caused by this action can be seen by observing the **photosphere**—the top surface of the convection zone—which gives the sun a **mottled** look.

What are the parts of the sun? After the core, the convection zone, and the photosphere, there is a spiked layer of gas called the **chromosphere.** It is about 6,000 miles (9,600 km) deep and has a temperature of about 54,000°F (30,000°C). It glows reddish during an eclipse. Around this layer is a faint crown of gas called the **corona.** Surprisingly the corona's temperature is 1,800,000°F (1,000,000°C), much hotter than that of the surface, which is almost 10,800°F (6,000°C). In order to maintain this temperature, a direct input of energy is necessary, but where it comes from is a mystery.

*What are **prominences, sunspots,** and **flares**?* The sun has a magnetic field. This great magnetic field is made up of many small magnetic areas which force their way out and spread over the surface. Stormy activity takes place where these magnetic fields are very strong. Sometimes the stormy activity takes the form of huge arches or graceful loops of gas called prominences, which reach tem-

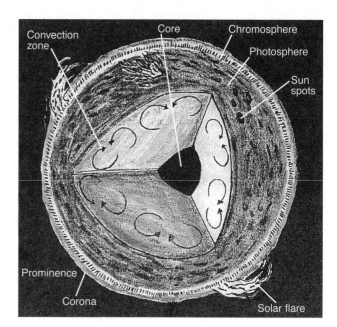

The parts of the sun

peratures as high as 10,000 Kelvins (units of temperature; room temperature is about 300 Kelvins). Sometimes these prominences last for several months, but usually they fall back into the sun within a few hours.

Sunspots, those dark spots that can be seen on the sun, contain strong magnetic fields. They vary in number; the largest number usually occur about every 11 years, as in 1991. About five times the earth's diameter, their powerful magnetic fields prevent the usual flow of energy upward, making the sun's surface cooler and thus darker where they are. Sunspots can trigger prominences and ignite solar flares (tremendous explosions). "When there are many sunspots, there are many prominences and flares. Sunspots announce the coming of storms on the sun. They are a storm alarm for the entire solar system.

"The sun's activity seems to bring about changes in the earth's climate. Astronomer John A. Eddy has shown that for 7,000 years glaciers on Earth have advanced and retreated in step with the sun's activity. When the sun is very active, the glaciers retreat. When it is fairly quiet, they advance again. So sunspots may well have far-reaching effects on all Earth's life, effects we are only now beginning to learn about."*

* From *Our Universe,* by Roy A. Gallant, published by The National Geographic Society, 1994. Reprinted with permission of The National Geographic Society.

What is sunlight? "The sunlight we see each day is made up of tiny units of radiant energy called **photons.** Born in the inferno of the sun's core, they spend millions of years slowly wandering up to the surface. Then, in eight minutes, they speed across the 93 million miles (150 million km) to Earth"*—a distance which is called an astronomical unit. This distance is equivalent to driving a car at 55 mph (88 kph) from the earth to the sun in 193 years.

Depending on the amount of energy a photon has, it may be absorbed by the earth's atmosphere. Or it may zip down to the earth's surface and help warm a flea or a blade of grass for a fraction of a second. Each photon carries only a tiny amount of energy, but trillions of them hit each square meter of Earth every second. Together they form sunlight. Of course, clouds, water, and the ground itself reflect a lot of sunlight back into space. It is this reflected sunlight that allows us to see Earth from a spaceship.

How big is the sun compared to Earth? It would require about 333,000 Earths to equal the sun's mass. But more than a million Earths could fit inside. This is because the sun's volume is greater than its mass. Solar matter averages one-fourth as

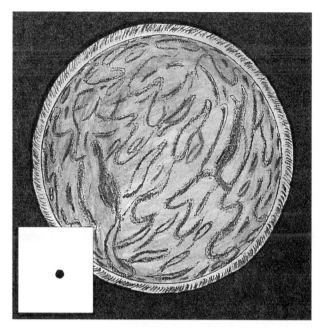

The size of the earth compared to the sun

dense as earthly matter. In terms of size, the sun dwarfs our planet. About 109 Earths could fit side by side across the diameter of the sun. If the sun was the size of a large orange, the earth would be the size of a tiny seed about 33 feet (10 m) away.

THINKING IT OVER

(1) What is one second of energy from the sun comparable to in terms of the amount of energy we use on

Earth? Give two examples: _____

_____

_____

(2) Give the parts of the sun, beginning from its core: _____

_____

(3) How often does the largest number of sunspots occur? _____

In 1997, when was the most recent year that this happened? _____

STUDYING THE PASSAGE

(1) Find the Main Idea: Choose one.
    (a) Why the sun is important to us.
    (b) How the sun regulates our weather.

* From *Our Universe* by Roy A. Gallant, published by The National Geographic Society, 1994. Reprinted with permission of The National Geographic Society.

(c) The energy of the sun.

(d) An explanation of the sun and how it functions.   _____

(2) Find the Facts: Mark each one *true* or *false*.

(a) The sun is a star.   _____

(b) The earth receives only about one-billionth of the total energy output of the sun.   _____

(c) The energy that the sun gives off is constantly changing.   _____

(d) The corona is hotter than the surface of the sun.   _____

(e) Stormy activity takes place where the magnetic field is strong.   _____

(f) Sunspots are thought to affect the amount of light Earth receives.   _____

(g) The sun's activity seems to bring about changes in the earth's climate.   _____

(h) Sunlight is made up of photons.   _____

(3) Find the Order: Number the following in the order in which they appear in the passage.

(a) Their powerful magnetic fields prevent the usual flow of energy upward, making the sun's surface cooler.   _____

(b) They spend millions of years slowly wandering up to the surface.   _____

(c) When the sun is very active, the glaciers retreat.   _____

(d) But more than a million Earths could fit inside.   _____

(e) Here, hydrogen atoms are fused into helium.   _____

(f) Sometimes the stormy activity takes the form of huge arches or graceful loops of gas.   _____

(g) There is a spiked layer of gas called the chromosphere.   _____

(h) The sun furnishes directly or indirectly all of the energy supporting life on Earth.   _____

(4) Go beyond the Facts: Which one would *not* be a conclusion you could reach from reading this passage?

(a) The sun is capable of sustaining life on many Earths.

(b) The sun's behavior remains constant, rarely changing.

(c) The photons that reach us are millions of years old.

(d) There are still parts of the sun we don't understand.   _____

(5) Determine the Writer's Style and Technique: The style of writing in this passage is most suited to:

(a) A journal for astronomers.

(b) A science textbook.

(c) A magazine.

(d) A newspaper.   _____

USING THE WORDS

(1) Words and Their Meanings: Find the boldfaced word for these definitions.

_____   (a) tiny units of radiant energy

_____   (b) huge arches or loops of gas

_____   (c) where energy is transported by currents of rising and sinking gas

_____   (d) dark spots thought to affect Earth's weather

_____   (e) a faint layer of gas with a higher temperature than the sun's surface

_____ (f) tremendous explosions that erupt from the sun's surface

_____ (g) a spiked layer of gas about 6,000 miles (9,600 km) deep

_____ (h) the top surface of the convection zone, which has a mottled look

_____ (i) having different-colored spots or blotches

(2) Write a paragraph using four of the words from the list above. Use a separate piece of paper.

WRITING ABOUT IT

Use a separate piece of paper.

(1) Explain why we are dependent on the sun for life. Then answer the questions in each of the headings in the passage.

(2) The sun has been a source of myths and legends since ancient times. Now you create a myth or story involving the sun.

CHEMICALS IN OUR FOOD

ABOUT THE PASSAGE   You probably sprinkle a little salt on your vegetables, put some sugar in your coffee or cocoa, add oregano or a dash of hot pepper to your pizza. But what about mixing mono- and diglycerides with your peanut butter or putting calcium propionate on your bread? These substances and thousands of others are common ingredients in many of our foods.

REASON FOR READING   To learn why chemicals are added to foods and what effect they may have.

READ THE PASSAGE

Adding substances to foods to give them color, enhance their flavor, and interrupt the **monotony** of eating the same foods day after day is not new. People in all parts of the world have done this for centuries. **Brine** has preserved meat for medieval serfs, Northwest Coast Native Americans, and small midwestern farmers; starch from vegetables has thickened soups and stews; herbs and spices have made sharp, sour, sweet, and **piquant** dishes; and plant extracts, such as saffron yellow, have added color to rice dishes. Indeed, the Americas were discovered by accident as ships searched for a shorter route to the East Indies and their much desired spices. Since the early twentieth century, however, the nature of substances added to food has changed dramatically. In addition to natural substances, another type of additives is now used. These are chemicals—synthetic substances made in a laboratory. Not only are chemicals added to foods, but entirely new foods have been made from chemicals.

Synthetic food additives were developed for several reasons. They made preparing food more convenient. People could shop for cake, bread mixes, boxed dry cereals, prepared dinners, fruits, and vegetables a week or more in advance instead of every two or three days. Women often prepared the meals, and more women were taking jobs outside of the home, so saving time was an important advantage to them. As more people moved from the country to urban homes, they grew less of their own food and depended more upon buying it in stores. To prevent packaged foods from spoiling on store shelves, chemicals were added.

Additives improved the qualities of some foods. A silicate added to salt or flour prevented caking. Mono- and diglycerides mixed with peanut butter prevented separation of oil and nuts. Calcium propionate prevented mold and a stale flavor in bread and rolls. Foods looked more attractive and **palatable** because of additives. Butter was tinted yellow to take away its pale white look. The nitrite compounds in frankfurters, ham, and luncheon meats replaced their grayish hue with a pink meat-like color and helped to protect consumers from botulism, a type of food poisoning that can be fatal.

But one of the most important reasons for using additives was that they were **lucrative.** Chemicals could be used to make entirely new foods: nondairy creamers and dessert toppings; soft drinks, diet soft drinks, and low-calorie protein drinks; and breakfast cereals. Then, too, manufacturers could substitute an inexpensive chemical for a more expensive natural product. Air and thickening agents were used for cream in ice cream, and lecithin replaced cocoa butter in chocolate bars. Manufacturers learned that with the help of advertising, people could be persuaded to buy only fruits and vegetables that looked perfect. They added an orange dye to oranges that had a mottled green and orange look when picked. Such a color additive was entirely for the sake of appearance.

Look at the ingredients in a common, familiar dessert—cherry Jell-O. The label reads: sugar, gelatin, adipic acid, disodium phosphate, fumaric acid, artificial flavor, artificial color, natural flavor. The only essential ingredients for making this dessert would be gelatin, sugar, and fruit. All of the other ingredients are included to preserve and maintain the Jell-O while it is sitting on the shelf awaiting use. All of these additives are described as GRAS (generally recognized as safe) by the Food and Drug Administration, but are nevertheless unnecessary for the dessert itself.

While adding things to food may originally have been a harmless or even **beneficial** custom, the addition of large amounts of chemicals to so many foods has raised questions. An informed researcher estimated that Americans consume annually about five pounds of chemicals and additives. Before 1958, the safety of many of the substances added was not systematically tested. They were not studied for their ability to cause cancer or to cause genes to **mutate** in later generations. But large numbers of birth defects and cases of cancer tied to the regular use of certain foods has made many people cautious about what they eat.

In 1938, in an attempt to provide some regulation, the federal Food, Drug, and Cosmetic Act was passed, but it was so weak that manufacturers could put anything they wished into food and could not be forced to remove it unless the substance was proven dangerous. Not until 1958 and 1960 did **amendments** require that a substance be shown safe before it may be added to foods. These amendments specif-

ically prohibit any chemical in food that causes cancer when fed at any level to animals or humans. Several coal tar dyes used to color food, the artificial sweetener cyclamate, and agene, a once-popular flour-bleaching agent that caused epileptic attacks in dogs, have been prohibited. However, two widely used additives suspected of being **carcinogenic**—nitrites in meats and saccharin, an artificial sweetener—are still in wide use.

Some consumers who believe that the Food and Drug Administration is not adequately regulating food additives are reading food labels carefully and are taking steps to get fresh, unprocessed food. Those living in urban areas are growing more of their own vegetables, even when the only land available may be a small patch in the front yard or a flat rooftop.

Farmers' markets are flourishing in several large cities. Farmers from surrounding areas drive into the city on certain days to sell their fresh produce. This provides small farmers with a market and an income so they can continue farming. It gives buyers fresh, unprocessed food without the added costs of cross-country transport. Many people are avoiding prepared, packaged foods and are returning to cooking dishes from "scratch." They prefer buying the separate ingredients so that they know the food is fresh and contains few or no additives.

THINKING IT OVER

(1) What are three reasons chemical additives are added to food? _____

_____

_____

STUDYING THE PASSAGE

(1) Find the Main Idea: Choose one.
   (a) Food additives are a recent thing.
   (b) People have always liked to add things to their food.
   (c) Some modern food additives are considered unsafe.
   (d) New foods have been made from chemicals.   ____

(2) Find the Facts: Mark each one *true* or *false*.
   (a) Adding things to food to improve their color or flavor began in the twentieth century.   ____
   (b) Oranges picked from the tree may be a mottled green and orange color.   ____
   (c) Food additives can prevent bread and rolls from becoming stale or moldy.   ____

(d) Brine is a method of preserving meat.   _____

(e) Cherry Jell-O contains sugar, gelatin, and cherries.   _____

(f) Some additives to flour caused epileptic attacks in children.   _____

(g) Color additives also provide nutritional benefits.   _____

(h) Brine is carcinogenic.   _____

(3) Find the Order: Number the following in the order in which they appear in the passage.

(a) Air and thickening agents are substituted for cream in ice cream.   _____

(b) Butter was tinted yellow.   _____

(c) Nothing that has caused cancer in animals or humans may be added to foods.   _____

(d) Some people are avoiding foods with additives.   _____

(e) Non-dairy dessert toppings are new foods made from chemicals.   _____

(f) Foods stay fresher longer if they have chemicals added.   _____

(g) Synthetic chemicals have been added to foods since the early twentieth century.   _____

(h) Saffron is used to give color to foods such as rice.   _____

(4) Go beyond the Facts: From the information given in this passage we can conclude that the writer:

(a) Believes food additives are one of the benefits of twentieth-century life.

(b) Believes food additives should be avoided totally.

(c) Believes food additives may be safe to a certain extent but should be used with care and caution.

(d) Has no opinion about food additives.   _____

(5) Determine the Writer's Style and Technique: This selection

(a) Uses comparison and contrast to define what something is.

(b) Uses humor and anecdotes to present the facts.

(c) Describes a process.

(d) Presents facts and details to define what something is.   _____

USING THE WORDS

(1) Words and Their Meanings: Find the boldfaced word for these definitions.

_____ (a) corrections; clauses added to a law to revise it

_____ (b) bringing in money; profitable

_____ (c) a tiresome sameness

_____ (d) savory; agreeably stimulating to the taste

_____ (e) to undergo significant and basic alteration

_____ (f) water strongly saturated with salt

_____ (g) leading to well-being

_____ (h) good-tasting

_____ (i) tending to produce cancer

(2) Write a paragraph using four of the words from the list above. Use a separate piece of paper.

WRITING ABOUT IT

Use a separate piece of paper.

(1) Reread the passage and underline, highlight, or make notes on the important facts. Then write a clear, conclusive summary of what it tells you about chemicals in our foods.

(2) Make a survey of the foods you and your family eat. Read the labels to find out which ingredients they contain. Then, using the information in your notes and summary, write a report on the chemicals in our food, giving the foods you eat as specific examples.

BUCK*

ABOUT THE PASSAGE   A respected, dignified, and loyal pet to a judge in southern California is stolen and transported to the hard conditions of the frozen wastelands of the Yukon to become a sled dog. What do you think happens?

REASON FOR READING   To see how scientific facts—in this case the accurate description of a sled dog's characteristics—can be woven into a fictional story to give it authenticity and meaning.

READ THE PASSAGE*

Day after day, for days unending, Buck toiled in the traces. Always, they broke camp in the dark, and the first gray of dawn found them hitting the trail with fresh miles reeled off behind them. And always they pitched camp after dark, eating their bit of fish, and crawling to sleep into the snow. Buck was ravenous. The pound and a half of sun-dried salmon, which was his ration for each day, seemed to go nowhere. He never had enough, and suffered from perpetual hunger pangs. Yet the other dogs, because they weighed less and were born to the life, received a pound only of the fish and managed to keep in good condition.

He swiftly lost the **fastidiousness** which had characterized his old life. A dainty eater, he found that his mates, finishing first, robbed him of his unfinished ration. There was no defending it. While he was fighting off two or three, it was disappearing down the throats of the others. To remedy this, he ate as fast as they; and, so greatly did hunger compel him, he was not above taking what did not belong to him. He watched and learned. When he saw Pike, one of the new dogs, a clever **malingerer** and thief, slyly steal a slice of bacon when Perrault's back was turned, he duplicated the performance the following day, getting away with the whole chunk. A great uproar was raised, but he was unsuspected, while Dub, an awkward blunderer who was always getting caught, was punished for Buck's misdeed.

This first theft marked Buck as fit to survive in the hostile Northland environment. It marked his adaptability, his capacity to adjust himself to changing conditions, the lack of which would have meant swift and terrible death. It marked, further, the decay or going to pieces of his moral nature, a vain thing and a handicap in the ruthless struggle for existence. It was all well enough in the Southland, under the law of love and fellowship, to respect private property and personal feelings; but in the Northland, under the law of club and fang, whoso took such things into account was a fool, and in so far as he observed them he would fail to prosper.

Not that Buck reasoned it out. He was fit, that was all, and unconsciously he accommodated himself to the new mode of life. All his days, no matter what the odds, he had never run from a fight. But the club of the man in the red sweater had beaten into him a more fundamental and primitive code. Civilized, he could have died for a moral consideration, say the defence of Judge Miller's riding whip; but the completeness of his decivilization was now evidenced by his ability to flee from the defence of a moral consideration and so save his hide. He did not steal for joy of it, but because of the clamor of his stomach. He did not rob openly, but stole secretly and cunningly, out of respect for club and fang. In short, the things he did were done because it was easier to do them than not to do them.

His development (or **retrogression**) was rapid. His muscles became hard as iron, and he grew **callous** to all ordinary pain. He achieved an internal as

*Reprinted by permission of Simon & Schuster. From *The Call of the Wild* by Jack London, copyright 1974.

well external economy. He could eat anything, no matter how loathsome or indigestible; and, once eaten, the juices of his stomach extracted the last least particle of nutriment; and his blood carried it to the farthest reaches of his body, building it into the toughest and stoutest of tissues. Sight and scent became remarkably keen, while his hearing developed such acuteness that in his sleep he heard the faintest sound and knew whether it heralded peace or peril. He learned to bite the ice out with his teeth when it collected between his toes; and when he was thirsty and there was a thick scum of ice over the water hole, he would break it by rearing and striking it with stiff fore legs. His most **conspicuous** trait was an ability to scent the wind and forecast it a night in advance. No matter how breathless the air when he dug his nest by tree or bank, the wind that later blew inevitably found him to **leeward,** sheltered and snug.

And not only did he learn by experience, but instincts long dead became alive again. The domesticated generations fell from him. In vague ways he remembered back to the youth of the breed, to the time the wild dogs ranged in packs through the **primeval** forest, and killed their meat as they ran it down. It was no task for him to learn to fight with cut and slash and the quick wolf snap. In this manner had fought forgotten ancestors. They quickened the old life within him, and the old tricks which they had stamped into the heredity of the breed were his tricks. They came to him without effort or discovery, as though they had been his always. And when, on the still cold nights, he pointed his nose at a star and howled long and wolflike, it was his ancestors, dead and dust, pointing nose at star and howling down through the centuries and through him. And his **cadences** were their cadences, the cadences which voiced their woe and what to them was the meaning of the stillness, and the cold, and dark.

THINKING IT OVER

(1) How did Buck adapt to the new environment? _____

_____

(2) What "marked Buck as fit to survive in the hostile Northland environment"? _____

_____

_____

(3) What do you think the expression "the law of the club and fang" means? _____

_____

_____

STUDYING THE PASSAGE

(1) Find the Main Idea: Choose one.
   (a) How to survive in the wilderness.
   (b) How a dog adapts to a new environment.
   (c) The effects of being hungry.
   (d) How innate instincts come alive in times of hardship.   _____

(2) Find the Facts: Mark each one *true* or *false*.
   (a) Buck was given more food than the other dogs.   _____
   (b) Buck was the only dog that had not been raised in the wilderness.   _____
   (c) Buck stole some salmon.   _____

(d) Another dog was punished for Buck's stealing. _____

(e) Buck stole to show the other dogs he had adapted to his new life. _____

(f) Buck was able to dig his nest so he was sheltered from the wind. _____

(g) Buck began to feel the primitive instincts of his forbears. _____

(h) Buck remained a civilized dog. _____

(3) Find the Order: Number the following in the order in which they appear in the passage.

(a) A great uproar was raised, but he was unsuspected. _____

(b) To remedy this, he ate as fast as they. _____

(c) He learned to bite the ice out with his teeth when it collected between his toes. _____

(d) It was all well enough in the Southland, under the law of love and fellowship. _____

(e) And his cadences were their cadences. _____

(f) And always they pitched camp after dark. _____

(g) The domesticated generations fell from him. _____

(h) He did not rob openly, but stole secretly and cunningly. _____

(4) Go beyond the Facts: From reading this passage, what do you think are the two main themes of the book, *The Call of the Wild*, in which Buck is the main character?

(a) Kindness wins out.

(b) There is goodness in every individual.

(c) Deep within every individual there lies a primitive beast.

(d) Survival of the fittest. _____ _____

(5) Determine the Writer's Style and Technique: The story is told from the point of view of:

(a) The owner of the dog.

(b) The dog.

(c) The author.

(d) None of the above. _____

USING THE WORDS

(1) Words and Their Meanings: Find the boldfaced word for these definitions.

_____ (a) unfeeling; not having any feeling for the suffering of others

_____ (b) in the same direction as the wind is blowing

_____ (c) very particular

_____ (d) of earliest times; very ancient

_____ (e) easy to see; plainly visible

_____ (f) regular rhythms; the rise or fall of the voice; final chords of a section of music

_____ (g) someone who pretends to be sick in order to keep from working or doing one's duty

_____ (h) moving backward, especially into an earlier or worse condition

(2) Write a paragraph using four of the words from the list above. Use a separate piece of paper.

WRITING ABOUT IT

Use a separate piece of paper.

(1) Describe how Buck begins to change and adapt to his new environment. Explain how he changes physically and mentally; how he learns to adapt through observation; describe his experiences and how his primitive instincts emerge. Comment also on the part Buck's personality plays in his transformation.

(2) How do we survive in our world today? What gets us through the day? Write about the special circumstances, difficulties, and hardships students face today and how they can be overcome. At the same time, point out the good things students have going for them and the advantages they have today.

HARVESTING THE SEA

ABOUT THE PASSAGE   As the population of the world explodes, it becomes increasingly difficult to produce enough food for everyone. One important source of food we are just beginning to explore is the sea.

REASON FOR READING   Notice how the passage is written. What do you gain most from reading it?
  (a) Specific knowledge of details and facts
  (b) Knowledge of general facts
  (c) Understanding of cause and effect
  (d) Ability to follow a comparison

READ THE PASSAGE

"The sea is the vast **reservoir** of nature," said Captain Nemo in *Twenty Thousand Leagues under the Sea*. Today, a little over one hundred years after these words were written, they have even greater meaning. With a large world population and a diminishing reserve of productive land and natural resources, people are turning to the oceans (about 70 percent of the earth's surface) as a source of food and energy.

What exactly are the resources in the sea? To begin with, seawater itself is a great resource, and when an economical way has been discovered to remove its salt, it will provide us with the water that our agricultural and industrial processes require in such great quantity. Minerals dissolved in the oceans and buried in their floors in the form of **nodules** are another resource. Manganese, copper, nickel, and cobalt are known to exist in the Pacific Ocean floor. Laws are now being formulated in the United Nations to regulate ocean mining.

Another great possibility of the sea lies in its potential as a food source. Of course, people have always eaten organisms from the sea; fish has long been a **staple** in the diets of such countries as China, Japan, and Norway. North Americans have long considered shrimp, lobster, salmon, and **sole** not only nutritious, but also exceptionally tasty fare. On the less glamorous (and less expensive) side, what would we do without tuna salad or a tuna sandwich on the menu?

Now that people have a greater need than ever before to obtain nutrition from the depths of the sea, many nations are searching for ways to enlarge its yield. One method involves increasing the nutrients in an area so that the organisms there will enlarge and multiply to provide a bigger catch. In open sea, this would be **prohibitively** costly, but scientists in the former Yugoslavia have been able to increase the growth of mussels and oysters by fertilizing a shallow bay. Another method is to "farm" the sea, to take organisms from one area and replant them in another spot. Americans are experimenting with growing plants on the bottom of the ocean, either underneath protective plastic domes or in freeflowing water. Other plants are suspended on **submerged** racks.

Marine biologists in Japan have refined a farming technique that is centuries old. Traditionally, the Japanese would trap small shrimp and artificially feed them in enclosed lagoons. This produced larger animals and made them easier to harvest. Recent research has now made it possible to eliminate the first step and raise shrimp in total captivity from egg to market size.

Besides shrimp, oysters, and mussels, several species of fish are currently raised as crops; salmon, for example, are cultivated on the west coast of North America. The Chinese are reported to have systematized raising freshwater carp to the extent that they now harvest over one million metric tons a year. In salty, shallow ponds and mangrove swamps of coastal Asian countries, traditional methods of culture yield from 300 to 1,500 pounds of fish an acre yearly. Clearly, shallow water farming is richly rewarding and has the potential to exceed the output of the best landbased farms. In fact, properly managed, an acre of water can produce at least ten times more protein a year than an acre of pastureland.

In some places seaweed is used as a food. South Wales is the center of British seaweed consumption. There a red seaweed called laver is collected at low tide and used to make a shiny, gelatinous mass called "laverbread," which is fried and eaten with bacon and eggs. The Japanese consume most of the seaweed eaten in the world. They prepare it in a variety of dishes. Hundreds of thousands of Japanese workers gather and process more than a million tons of laver every year. A growing portion of this harvest is produced from farming operations.

Across the Pacific, Americans use floating mechanical reapers to cut giant kelp, a brown seaweed which occurs in great natural beds off the California coast. **Fronds** of this kelp may reach up to two hundred feet in length, and it grows faster than any other plant in the world—as much as two feet in a single day. An important product, algin (or alginic acid), is found in the plant's cell walls. As thickeners, coagulants, and **emulsifiers,** algin derivatives appear on the labels of soups, sauces, and mayonnaise; they also control the **viscosity** of salad dressings and fruit syrups. However, by far the largest amounts are used in making ice cream, to prevent crystals from forming and keep the fat from separating. All together, chemicals derived from algae smooth or thicken hundreds of preparations ranging from cream cheese dips to toothpaste.

It appears that the time is fast approaching when harvesting ocean crops will be common practice, and in the years to come we may even find our ocean farmers actually living in communities under the sea. The thought of huge domes covering human cities in deep waters sounds like science fiction to us today. But do not forget that many of Jules Verne's seemingly impossible ideas in *Twenty Thousand Leagues under the Sea* and other novels have actually become realities.

THINKING IT OVER

(1) What are three resources available from the sea? _____

_____

_____

STUDYING THE PASSAGE

(1) Find the Main Idea: Choose one.
   (a) Many of Jules Verne's predictions are coming true.
   (b) Important mineral deposits lie beneath the floor of the sea.
   (c) Fish farms will increase the world's food supply.
   (d) Human beings are finding new ways to develop the resources of the sea. _____

(2) Find the Facts: Mark each one *true* or *false*.
   (a) The oceans make up 70 percent of the earth's surface. _____
   (b) Shrimp farming is a recent idea in Japan. _____
   (c) Giant kelp can grow as fast as two feet a day. _____
   (d) The main consumers of seaweed are the Japanese. _____
   (e) Ice cream manufacturers use chemicals derived from a red seaweed called laver. _____
   (f) "Farming" the sea involves taking organisms from one area and replanting them in another spot. _____
   (g) Manganese, copper, nickel, and cobalt are known to exist in the ocean floor. _____
   (h) Scientists have been fertilizing the waters of shallow bays to increase the yield of oysters. _____

(3) Find the Order: Number the following in the order in which they appear in the passage.

    (a) Seawater itself is a great resource.   _____

    (b) One method is to increase the nutrients in an area.   _____

    (c) The United Nations is formulating laws to regulate mining of the ocean floors.   _____

    (d) Plastic domes protect plants growing on the ocean floor.   _____

    (e) People have always eaten organisms from the sea.   _____

    (f) Parts of seaweed are used in making ice cream.   _____

    (g) Mechanical reapers are used to harvest giant kelp.   _____

    (h) An acre of water can produce more protein than an acre of pastureland.   _____

(4) Go beyond the Facts: A problem now preventing us from using seawater for irrigation is that:

    (a) The process of removing salt is expensive.

    (b) There is not enough seawater available.

    (c) No process to remove the salt has been discovered.

    (d) There is not enough demand for fresh water.   _____

(5) Determine the Writer's Style and Technique: Choose one.

    (a) Gives specific details and facts.

    (b) Gives general facts.

    (c) Shows cause and effect.

    (d) Gives a comparison.   _____

USING THE WORDS

(1) Words and Their Meanings: Find the boldfaced word for these definitions.

_____   (a) placed under water

_____   (b) an item in steady demand by consumers, such as coffee, tea, flour, or salt

_____   (c) discouragingly, forbiddingly

_____   (d) chemical agents that cause particles to remain evenly distributed throughout a liquid

_____   (e) a large supply of water; a reserve

_____   (f) thickness or stickiness of a liquid; resistance to flowing or being poured

_____   (g) large leaflike structures

_____   (h) a flattened fish that swims on its side, resembling and related to the flounder

_____   (i) small lumps; small knoblike growths

(2) Write a paragraph using four of the words from the list above. Use a separate piece of paper.

WRITING ABOUT IT

Use a separate piece of paper.

(1) Reread the passage, noting the important parts. Then rewrite the passage as an editorial in a newspaper, emphasizing the idea that we should use the sea more for our benefit and to feed the many starving people in the world.

(2) The passage talks about the sea from a practical point of view. Write about the sea from an aesthetic point of view. Describe the sea as vividly and descriptively as you can. Choose a particular time of day, a specific location, the kind of weather, and the mood you want to create—romantic, happy, sad, frightening, relaxed, tranquil, etc. Try to make your reader see and hear the water and sense the mood by appealing to all the senses.

THE HIGH WAY

ABOUT THE PASSAGE

Your attitude to transportation may be, "Who cares how it works as long as it gets me there." However, in regard to air transportation one cannot help but be in awe of what humans have achieved. Through ingenuity, people have made it possible for a tank of jet fuel to propel a mammoth aircraft full of passengers and cargo into the sky, and literally use the sky as a highway.

REASON FOR READING

This explanation needs to be read slowly and carefully. When you have finished, see if you can explain the underlying principles of air and space travel.

READ THE PASSAGE

For centuries people have looked to the sky as a frontier to be conquered. Envious of the birds, we have constantly sought ways to claim their domain as our own.

Tales of attempts to challenge the sky include the myth of Daedalus and Icarus. This father and son, imprisoned on an island, escaped using wings made from feathers and beeswax. They jumped from a high cliff and sailed off into the bright blue sky. However, Icarus **rashly** flew too near the sun and its heat melted the wax. His wings disintegrated and he fell to his death. Most of the actual early attempts to fly were more reasonable, although equally unsuccessful. It was not until the Wright brothers made their historic flight at Kitty Hawk that the sky was truly conquered.

An important factor in the Wright brothers' success was the development of the internal **combustion** engine, which is small, light, and, for its size, very powerful. This type of engine transmits power from pistons to a crankshaft used to turn a propeller. The spinning propeller provides the tremendous thrust necessary to move the plane forward. However, maximum speed for a propeller plane is about 400 miles an hour. At higher speeds, air rushes into the blades so fast that they hardly have time to throw it backward. As a result, the faster the airplane moves, the less the thrust.

In an effort to increase airspeed beyond the lim-

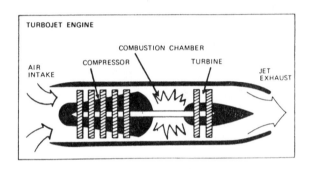

its of the propeller, the turbojet engine was developed. All **propulsion** depends on Newton's third law of motion, and the jet engine takes direct advantage of this principle that "for every action, there is an equal and opposite reaction." The turbojet engine eliminates the need for propellers; it does the job of throwing air backward in a different way. Air is pulled or sucked in from the front of the engine and enters a compressor, where it is put under high pressure. From here, the compressed air is forced into the combustion chamber, into which fuel is sprayed and ignited. The hot, burning gases expand with great force. In a conventional engine, like that in a propeller plane or an automobile, this explosion pushes a piston, but in the jet, there are no pistons. Instead, the expanding gases push against the whole interior of the engine, in a sense, as they force their way out through a small nozzle at the rear. The action of the exhaust moving out of the plane at speeds up to 2,000 miles an hour produces an "opposite reaction," causing the plane itself to thrust forward. A small part of the exhaust energy also spins turbine blades which, in turn, drive the compressor up front, so that the whole process is continuous. And the faster the air enters the compressor, the greater the force developed when it burns with the fuel. Thus with the jet, the greater the speed, the greater the thrust.

The basic principle of the jet engine is also applied in the **satellites** and spacecraft that we have used to penetrate the world of outer space. As in a jet, fuel is burned in a closed space so that exhaust gases blast out through a nozzle with great force. This principle works in a **vacuum** just as well as in an atmosphere; the reason is that the escaping gas does not push against anything behind the rocket in order to create the forward thrust. It is simply the action of the escaping gas, setting up an equal and opposite reaction, that causes the forward motion of the object.

However, the rocket is unique in that no air is needed to burn the fuel. Whereas the "air-breathing" jet can operate only up to altitudes of some 90,000 feet before it runs out of oxygen, rockets can travel anywhere. This is because they carry both fuel and their own supply of **oxidizer** for combustion. Such propellant mixtures may consist of nitro explosives, liquid oxygen and kerosene, or liquid oxygen and hydrogen. In this respect, a space rocket is just a highly sophisticated cousin of the skyrocket we fire on the Fourth of July. Inside the sealed skyrocket tube is a small amount of fuel and oxidizer mixture called gunpowder. On the tail is a

fuse, which when lit bores its way into the powder, causing it to ignite. Hot, expanding gases produced by the burning powder rush out of the hole left by the burned fuse. The rocket reacts by soaring through the air until the powder is **exhausted.** This is rocket propulsion, the most elementary principle upon which feats of space exploration such as moon landings are based.

Liquid-fuel rocket engines operate in much the same manner as the solid-fuel skyrocket. In the liquid-fuel engine, the fuel and oxides (usually liquid oxygen) are pumped into a combustion chamber, where they are ignited. The resultant exploding gases exit through a nozzle, and forward jet thrust is produced.

Having solved the problem of getting spacecraft into outer space, the next problem astronautical engineers had to overcome was slowing down and landing the craft. However, this was not as difficult as it may seem, for the blast of gas can be used to slow a vehicle down as well as to increase its speed. In order to break its headlong dash, the spacecraft is fitted with a mechanism to rotate it so that it approaches the surface of the moon, or wherever it is landing, tail first. Here again, Newton's law is applied. The astronauts start the engines, which emit a blast of gas that streams downward toward the landing site. This is the action. The opposite and equal reaction is the exhaust's push upward toward the spacecraft. This upward force is so great that it partially counteracts the speed of the vehicle's fall and automatically slows it down. The blast of gas from the tail is gradually increased until the force of the fall is nearly equaled by the force of the blast from the motors. This balance slows the craft, and it settles gently on the ground.

We have come a long way from attaching birds' feathers to our bodies to conquer the great realms of space. Now we can go almost anywhere our **whims** take us—as long as we have and are willing to spend the astronomical amounts of money necessary to build the vehicles and powerful engines to take us into that ocean of emptiness.

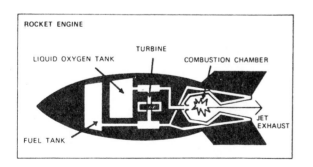

ROCKET ENGINE

LIQUID OXYGEN TANK   TURBINE   COMBUSTION CHAMBER

JET EXHAUST

FUEL TANK

THINKING IT OVER

(1) State the fundamental principle of propulsion. _____

_____

_____

_____

(2) After whom is this principle named? _____

(3) How does a piston engine driving a propeller differ from a turbojet engine? How do both of these differ

from a rocket engine? _____

_____

_____

_____

_____

_____

STUDYING THE PASSAGE

(1) Find the Main Idea: Choose one.
   (a) Development of air travel has progressed fantastically.
   (b) Space travel is now as easy as intercontinental travel.
   (c) Rocket engines and skyrockets are really very similar.
   (d) New methods of propulsion have enabled us to conquer the sky and explore outer space. _____

(2) Find the Facts: Mark each one *true* or *false*.
   (a) Daedalus and Icarus flew by harnessing pigeons to their arms. _____
   (b) The Wright brothers were the first to fly an airplane successfully. _____
   (c) The propeller-driven plane can only fly up to speeds of about 400 miles an hour. _____
   (d) The jet engine cannot operate very far above 90,000 feet. _____
   (e) Newton's third law of motion is that for every action there is an equal and opposite reaction. _____
   (f) Spacecraft have to carry their own source of oxygen for burning their fuel. _____
   (g) It is the action of escaping gases that causes a rocket to thrust into the air. _____
   (h) Landing a spacecraft uses the same principle as that employed to launch it. _____

(3) Find the Order: Number the following in the order in which they appear in the passage.
   (a) The greater the speed, the less the thrust. _____
   (b) Inside the tube there is a small amount of gunpowder. _____
   (c) It does the job of pushing air backward in a different way. _____
   (d) The engine's crankshaft is used to turn the propeller. _____
   (e) They jumped from a high cliff. _____
   (f) This principle works as well in a vacuum as it does in an atmosphere. _____
   (g) In order to break its headlong dash, the spacecraft is fitted with a mechanism. _____
   (h) Now we can go almost anywhere our whims take us. _____

(4) Go beyond the Facts: Which of the following conclusions are suggested by the passage? (Choose more than one.)
   (a) Interplanetary travel could be part of our future.
   (b) The United States has spent too much money on the conquest of space.
   (c) We will need larger airports in the future.
   (d) New inventions are often based on well-known, long-established principles.   ____   ____

(5) Determine the Writer's Style and Technique: Choose one.
   (a) Describes scientific principles.
   (b) Tells a story.
   (c) Uses examples to show how something works.
   (d) Presents an argument.   ____

USING THE WORDS

(1) Words and Their Meanings: Find the boldfaced word for these definitions.

   _____   (a) the action or process of propelling

   _____   (b) too hastily or recklessly

   _____   (c) manmade or natural objects that orbit the earth, the moon, or another celestial body

   _____   (d) used up

   _____   (e) a substance that oxidizes something (combines it chemically with oxygen)

   _____   (f) a space absolutely devoid of matter

   _____   (g) notions, fancies

   _____   (h) the act or process of burning; violent agitation

(2) Write a paragraph using four of the words from the list above. Use a separate piece of paper.

WRITING ABOUT IT

Use a separate piece of paper.

(1) Explain how a piston engine driving a propeller differs from a turbojet engine. Then explain how they both differ from a rocket engine.

(2) If you were going on a journey of your own choice, which method of transportation would you choose? Describe your journey in detail—it may be any distance and the means of transportation may be your own two feet, an animal, the subway, a spacecraft, etc.

THE WRESTLING MATCH*

ABOUT THE PASSAGE	Why is the boy in this story so adamant about representing his class in a wrestling match? What do you learn about him halfway through that is surprising?
REASON FOR READING	To think about people's characteristics and why they act the way they do.

READ THE PASSAGE

Doug, Frank, and I went over to the chapel for the first official meeting of our freshman class. We sat quietly through the long speeches from college **dignitaries.** The **sermonizing** over, the Dean rose to tell us of the Freshman-Sophomore Day to be held that Saturday. It was to consist of an athletic competition, and, to my great joy, one of the events was to be wrestling. There were to be three bouts, a lightweight, middleweight, and heavyweight, and the Dean called for volunteers to represent us in these divisions.

With my heart in my mouth and supporting myself by hanging onto the back of the seat in front of me, I volunteered as the freshman heavyweight and sank back into my seat. My proposal was greeted with a **stunned** silence from my hundred and thirty classmates. As the silence thickened, I realized they were probably trying to think of how to reject my offer without publicly embarrassing me.

During the next days I went through the regular "freshman orientation," but I recall only the afternoons I spent in the gym trying to **limber** up my stiff muscles for Saturday.

Our class won the first event and kept on winning. Doug was trying to explain to me what was happening when he was interrupted by our temporary class president, a big football player, who tapped me on the shoulder and took me aside.

"Look, Bob," he said, "the sophomores have put up a huge tackle from last year's team. We all think it's great of you to have offered to wrestle for us, but it's not too late to change your mind. I've been working out this last week, and I'm all ready to go. What do you say?"

I realized no one had taken my offer seriously. They never really expected me to go through with it, and they had quietly selected a substitute in whom they had placed their confidence.

"No," I answered. "If you wanted to wrestle, you should have challenged me before today. Since you didn't, you have no right to take my place." I was very nervous, as I always was before a match, but I knew that more was riding on this bout than on any I had ever wrestled before.

"Nobody will think badly of you," he continued; "don't be afraid of that."

But I didn't want them simply not to think badly of me. I wanted them to think well of me.

"No! I'm going to wrestle."

"Well, okay, then. Good luck."

My turn came at last, and I walked to the center of the clearing in the crowd. The referee asked for silence so that I could hear the footsteps of my adversary as we approached each other. He need not have asked because as I walked out a hush fell over the field.

As soon as we came together, I knew I would have my hands full: my opponent outweighed me by thirty-five pounds, none of which was fat. Not knowing what would really be **cricket** for him to do, he felt the awkwardness of his position. This uncertainty was his downfall, for I was merciless. I tripped him quickly and, as he fell, slipped a half nelson on and rolled him over onto his back. He struggled furiously when he understood what was happening, but

*From *To Catch an Angel* by Robert Russell, Vanguard Press, Inc., 1962.

it was too late. The crowd burst into cheers while the referee pounded the turf to signify a fall.

However, the rules called for two out of three falls, so the match was far from over. I knew that in the second bout he would have no **qualms** about my blindness and was probably furious at his public humiliation, so the minute's rest between bouts gave me much-needed time to consider how I should try to handle him.

"All right," cried the referee, "time's up," and we started again at each other across the grass. I proceeded warily toward the sound of his footsteps, but all my caution was useless. With a tremendous charge he sent me sprawling and was on me like a tiger. His strength and anger made him impossible to handle, so I let him shove me about without trying to match the **fury** of his attack. It would have been useless for me to try out-muscling him; I simply had to wait until he gave me an opening.

Finally it came. He reached an arm under mine in an attempt to turn me over. I clamped down on his arm above the elbow and put all my strength into a roll that carried me around, dragging him beneath me. I quickly turned, let go his arm, and I was on top. Immediately I put a scissors grip on him and flattened him. When he tried to get onto his hands and knees, I kicked his legs out from under him, at the same time knocking his arms forward. Again he found himself on his stomach.

After several **futile** attempts to get up, he started to roll furiously in the hope of doing to me what I had done to him. He was much too big and too powerful for me to stop these rolls; instead, I simply gave his roll added impetus so that in place of a half roll, which would have left him on top of me, we performed a complete turn so that he was still on the bottom. After he had tired himself out in these struggles, I put on a half nelson and turned him over, and pinned him again.

The crowd roared once more, and the referee raised my arm in victory. There seemed to be hundreds of people pounding me on the back, shaking my hands, and practically carrying me from the field of battle. That day, when the shoulders of the big tackle pressed against the grass for the second time, I began to win a place at Hamilton.

If I had passed up my chance to wrestle, I might have passed up a college career and much more besides. It was a chance to make a definite, violent, and public declaration that I was not peculiar, not weak or afraid, and would not be ignored; that I neither expected nor would accept any concessions to my blindness.

THINKING IT OVER

(1) Why did the boy want to represent his class in the wrestling match? _____

_____

_____

(2) What do you learn about halfway through that is surprising? _____

_____

(3) How many bouts did it take to win the wrestling match? _____

STUDYING THE PASSAGE

(1) Find the Main Idea: Choose one.
    (a) Why wrestling is a good sport for a blind boy.
    (b) How a blind boy's classmates considered him different.
    (c) How a blind boy won a wrestling match.
    (d) How a blind boy proved himself.   _____

(2) Find the Facts: Mark each one *true* or *false*.
    (a) The first official meeting of the freshman class was in the auditorium. _____
    (b) The Freshman-Sophomore Day was on Saturday. _____
    (c) The events of the Freshman-Sophomore Day were to be just wrestling matches. _____
    (d) The narrator volunteered as the freshman lightweight. _____
    (e) The narrator expected his classmates to be surprised at his volunteering. _____
    (f) The freshmen had found someone to replace the narrator in the match. _____
    (g) The narrator's opponent outweighed him by thirty-five pounds. _____
    (h) Winning the wrestling match changed his classmates' attitude toward him. _____

(3) Find the Order: Number the following in the order in which they appear in the passage.
    (a) Again he found himself on his stomach. _____
    (b) Doug was trying to explain to me what was happening. _____
    (c) It was a chance to make a definite, violent, and public declaration. _____
    (d) With my heart in my mouth. _____
    (e) I realized no one had taken my offer seriously. _____
    (f) We sat quietly through the long speeches from college dignitaries. _____
    (g) As I walked out a hush fell over the field. _____
    (h) I recall only the afternoons I spent in the gym. _____

(4) Go beyond the Facts: The narrator wanted to win the wrestling match because he thought it would:
    (a) Win the sympathy of his classmates.
    (b) Win the friendship of his classmates.
    (c) Win the respect of his classmates.
    (d) Show his classmates how strong and powerful he was. _____

(5) Determine the Writer's Style and Technique: Which one does the writer *not* do?
    (a) Relate a series of events in chronological order.
    (b) Give the climax of the story in the middle.
    (c) Write the story as if it were an autobiography.
    (d) Explain a problem that is resolved. _____

USING THE WORDS

(1) Words and Their Meanings: Find the boldfaced word for these definitions.

_____ (a) fair play; sportsmanlike

_____ (b) ineffectual; useless

_____ (c) people holding a high position in government, school, etc.

_____ (d) bewildered; astounded; dumbfounded

_____ (e) speaking that is like a sermon

_____ (f) bending easily, flexible

_____ (g) rage; frenzy; turbulence

_____ (h) misgivings; uneasiness

(2) Write a paragraph using four of the words from the list above. Use a separate piece of paper.

WRITING ABOUT IT

Use a separate piece of paper.

The writer of this passage relates a series of events which easily and naturally led up to the climax and resolution of the story. When you write these assignments try to do the same thing. Think about the events and then write them down to make sure they follow an orderly sequence and lead to an appropriate ending. (It usually helps to think of the ending first.)

(1) Write a story in which you tell how you, or someone else, volunteers to do something that others feel you, or the person, could not or should not do.

(2) Write a story or a series of events that explains a person's feelings toward someone who is handicapped.

YOUR HEART*

ABOUT THE PASSAGE

In Selection 3 you learned about the body's cardiovascular system. In this selection you learn about the most remarkable organ that controls that system—your heart. How big is it? What makes it beat?

REASON FOR READING

To practice reading a detailed explanation.

READ THE PASSAGE

The heart—a simple pump and powerful machine only the size of a large fist—rules over

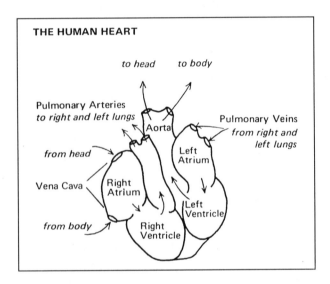

THE HUMAN HEART

to head   to body

Pulmonary Arteries
to right and left lungs

Aorta

Pulmonary Veins
from right and left lungs

from head

Left Atrium

Vena Cava

Right Atrium

Left Ventricle

from body

Right Ventricle

the body's circulation with steadfastness and strength. It begins to beat just four weeks after conception. With every beat, the adult heart expels 2 ounces of oxygen-rich blood, 5 quarts a minute, 220 million quarts over 70 years of life. Leg muscles soon tire when we run at top speed, but heart muscle works twice as hard when we relax, even harder when we exercise, never pausing for rest or repair. When surgeons replace heart valves with **silicone** parts, the hard, man-made materials become battered out of shape after only a few years. Yet the delicate, **durable** tissues of a healthy heart exert their force, and withstand the beating, for a lifetime.

The living **dynamo** that pumps with such power also pumps with **precision.** The heart must drive blood through our bodies with enough force to send it surging to the farthest capillary; yet it must pump blood gently to the lungs. If the heart sent blood through lung capillaries and into the air sacs with the same force that it pumps blood through other parts, we would drown in our own plasma. So our one heart, divided by a wall down the middle, has two sides. Each side contains two chambers: an atrium, or receiving tank, at the top, and a ventricle, the pump itself, at the bottom. The left ventricle, which sends blood through the body, has four times the muscle of its counterpart on the right. That is why we feel our heartbeat on the left side even though a third of the heart lies in the right side of the chest.

Though the left and right ventricles flex with different forces, they nonetheless beat at the same time, ensuring a blood flow that is smooth and continuous. Nature ensures this **synchrony** by wrapping both pumps in one muscle. **Spiraled** around the organ, this muscle wrings blood out of the heart, simultaneously emptying both pumps.

The contraction of the heart is one of its independent powers. It begins to beat in the embryo before any nerves connect it to the brain. In transplant surgery (see Selection 9) it even continues to throb after all nerves have been severed and the diseased organ removed from the chest. Even a single heart cell alone on a microscope slide pulsates as long as it has a fresh supply of blood.

This relentless pulse proves that the heart's beat originates from some power in its tissues. Every cardiac cell is, in fact, a living battery, crackling with chemically created energy that stimulates the movement we call a heartbeat. The heart cell generates electricity through two elements plentifully supplied in blood: sodium and potassium. The atoms that make up both elements frequently lose a negatively charged electron, leaving them with an extra proton, or a positive charge. These "charged" atoms are called ions.

Heart cells contain a high concentration of potassium ions, while the liquid surrounding the cells abounds in sodium. The cell membrane constantly pumps sodium out of the cardiac muscles and potassium into them. Because the membrane pumps sodium out faster than it pumps potassium in, an excess positive charge builds outside the cell. When it reaches a certain threshold, the flow suddenly reverses and sodium ions rush back into the cells. This sudden shift sparks an electric charge, and the heart cell **flinches** in contraction.

When scattered sparsely across a microscope slide, individual cardiac cells beat at different rates, but as they multiply and join, they form a single heaving sheet. Thus do heart cells behave in the human chest: they do not pulsate **discordantly,** each sparking to its own beat; they explode in rhythmic harmony. Buried high in the right atrium, a minute knot of cells sets the heart's pace. Called the sinus node, its sparks send electrical impulses racing through the heart to other electrical cells woven throughout cardiac tissue. In perfect rhythm each successively explodes. This trail of electricity flashes so rapidly across the heart that all its cells appear to beat as one.

The heart is most remarkable because it lasts so long. "Heart attack," an often misused term for a specific type of cardiac malfunction, is rarely caused by the heart itself. Strictly defined, a heart attack occurs when a patch of heart muscle dies. Most heart attacks stem from cardiovascular disease, primarily atherosclerosis.

Atherosclerosis is caused by droplets of cholesterol hardening the arteries' walls or even blocking the arteries. If atherosclerosis blocks either of the heart's two arteries—called coronary because they encircle the heart like a crown—heart muscle may die from lack of blood supply.

What makes a person a likely candidate for a heart attack? Studies show that no single factor causes heart disease, but rather a combination of many. However, high blood cholesterol has proved so important a cause that the higher a person's is, the higher the chance of disease, regardless of whether or not the person smokes or has high blood pressure—the next most important causes.

How can you prevent a heart attack? No one can guarantee you will not have a heart attack. But there are steps you can take which can lessen the possibility of having one. As cholesterol is such an important factor, the most obvious step to take is to cut down on cholesterol-high foods, namely animal products such as eggs, cheese, and whole milk and meat. It is also important to generally eat a sensible diet, have plenty of exercise, and not smoke.

THINKING IT OVER

(1) How big is the heart? _____

(2) What makes the heart beat? _____

_____

_____

_____

(3) What is the sinus node? _____

_____

STUDYING THE PASSAGE

(1) Find the Main Idea: Choose one.
    (a) How to prevent heart attacks.
    (b) How durable the heart is.
    (c) How remarkable the heart is.
    (d) How the heart functions.   _____

(2) Find the Facts: Mark each one *true* or *false*.
    (a) The heart begins to beat four months after conception.   _____
    (b) The heart expels five quarts of oxygen-rich blood every minute.   _____
    (c) The heart needs to vary the force of the blood.   _____
    (d) The left ventricle sends blood to the lungs.   _____
    (e) The brain controls the contractions of the heart.   _____
    (f) Each heart cell has the ability to pulsate.   _____
    (g) A heart attack occurs when heart muscle dies.   _____
    (h) Cholesterol is a cause of heart attacks.   _____

(3) Find the Order: Number the following in the order in which they appear in the passage.
    (a) Heart muscle works twice as hard when we relax, even harder when we exercise.   _____
    (b) It even continues to throb after all nerves have been severed.   _____
    (c) Nature ensures this synchrony by wrapping both pumps in one muscle.   _____
    (d) Thus do heart cells behave in the human chest.   _____
    (e) Heart cells contain a high concentration of potassium ions.   _____
    (f) The living dynamo that pumps with such power also pumps with precision.   _____
    (g) Most heart attacks stem from cardiovascular disease, primarily atherosclerosis.   _____
    (h) No one can guarantee you will not have a heart attack.   _____

(4) Go beyond the Facts: Which of the following people would be the least likely to have a heart attack?
    (a) Stefan exercises every day, has fried eggs, bacon, and toast for breakfast
        and does not smoke.
    (b) Tom never exercises, eats a mainly rice diet, and goes to bed at a reasonable hour.
    (c) Sarah stays up at night watching the late movies, eats a healthy diet, and goes
        jogging after dinner.
    (d) Elisa is very laid back, eats whatever food is available, and has taken up smoking.   _____

(5) Determine the Writer's Style and Technique:
    (a) Uses highly technical language to give a scientific explanation.
    (b) Uses everyday language to give a scientific explanation.
    (c) Uses an informal, conversational tone.
    (d) Uses unusual examples.   _____

USING THE WORDS

(1) Words and Their Meanings: Find the boldfaced word for these definitions.

_____   (a) lasting in spite of hard wear or much use

_____   (b) not agreeing or going well together; not in harmony

_____   (c) happening at the same time; moving at the same speed

_____   (d) draws back from a blow or from anything difficult or painful

_____   (e) exactness; accuracy

_____   (f) circled around a center in a curve

_____   (g) very forceful, energetic person or thing

_____   (h) a substance containing silicon—a chemical element that is not a
                                 metal and is always combined with something else

(2) Write a paragraph using four of the words from the list above. Use a separate piece of paper.

WRITING ABOUT IT

Use a separate piece of paper.

(1) Reread the passage to make sure you understand all the information. Make notes if necessary. Then make up a test of twelve questions (with the answers) covering the important facts. Have a partner do the same. Then trade tests to see if you can answer each other's questions.

(2) You have just read a scientific explanation of the heart. However, the heart can be described and interpreted in many other ways. For example, the heart has long been considered the source of one's affection (see Selection 4 on valentines). The heart is also evoked in many different expressions, such as, affairs of the heart; my heartfelt thanks; have a heart. Think about the different ways you can write about the heart. Jot down your ideas, then write an essay on the heart, giving it an appropriate title.

A PSALM OF LIFE

ABOUT THE PASSAGE   The writer of this poem was the most popular American poet of his century. What advice does he give us? Although he died in 1882, do you think his view is akin to our present-day concept of life?

REASON FOR READING   Longfellow's works were admired for their moral sentiments and their simple language set in strong, rhythmical lines. What other features make this poem effective? What does the message gain from being put into poetry?

READ THE PASSAGE

Tell me not, in mournful **numbers,**
    Life is but an empty dream!—
For the soul is dead that slumbers,
    And things are not what they seem.

Life is real! Life is **earnest!**
    And the grave is not its goal;
Dust thou art, to dust returnest,
    Was not spoken of the soul.

Not enjoyment, and not sorrow,
    Is our **destined** end or way;
But to act, that each to-morrow
    Find us farther than to-day.

Art is long, and Time is fleeting,
    And our hearts, though stout and brave,
Still, like **muffled** drums, are beating
    Funeral marches to the grave.

In the world's broad field of battle,
    In the **bivouac** of Life,
Be not like dumb, driven cattle!
    Be a hero in the strife!

Trust no Future, howe'er pleasant!
    Let the dead Past bury its dead!
Act,—act in the living Present!
    Heart within, and God o'erhead!

Lives of great men all remind us
    We can make our lives **sublime,**
And, departing, leave behind us
    Footprints on the sands of time:

Footprints, that perhaps another,
    Sailing o'er life's solemn main,
A **forlorn** and shipwrecked brother,
    Seeing, shall **take heart** again.

Let us, then, be up and doing,
    With a heart for any fate;
Still achieving, still pursuing,
    Learn to labor and to wait.

—Henry Wadsworth Longfellow

THINKING IT OVER

(1) Which stanza best seems to sum up the advice Longfellow gives us? _____

_____

(2) Did you notice how Longfellow makes good use of comparisons (metaphors, similes) to create vivid images (pictures) in this poem? Give three examples that you feel are particularly effective.

_____

_____

_____

STUDYING THE PASSAGE

(1) Find the Main Idea: Choose one.
   (a) Don't be afraid of death.
   (b) Live your life to the fullest.
   (c) Everyone must die sooner or later.
   (d) We should pattern our lives after successful people of the past.   _____

(2) Find the Facts: Mark each one *true* or *false*.
   (a) Life is meaningless, like an empty dream.   _____
   (b) The grave is really the only goal of each person's life.   _____
   (c) Each day should bring a little progress.   _____
   (d) The poet compares our heartbeats to drums in a funeral march.   _____
   (e) The poet suggests that people should live like cattle.   _____
   (f) The future is more important than the past or present.   _____
   (g) Our good example in life may someday help others.   _____
   (h) The last stanza means "All right, let's get to work; let's really try."   _____

(3) Find the Order: Number the following ideas in the order in which they appear in the passage.
   (a) Acting to achieve progress is the object of life.   _____
   (b) Someday maybe our own lives will be an example to help others.   _____
   (c) Unfortunately, some people live as though they are merely marking time before dying. _____
   (d) We must not just plod through life like animals.   _____
   (e) Your soul lives—it is not just dust.   _____
   (f) We study great people of the past to help guide our lives.   _____
   (g) We should not say that life is empty and useless.   _____
   (h) Live fully with God to guide you.   _____

(4) Go beyond the Facts: After reading this poem, which idea do you think Longfellow would agree with?
   (Choose one.)
   (a) Life is worth living well.
   (b) Life is a battle for survival.
   (c) Kindness and love for others is the greatest virtue.
   (d) Death comes too soon.   _____

(5) Determine the Writer's Style and Technique: Choose more than one. The poet:
   (a) Uses the device of personification.
   (b) Uses mainly common, everyday words.
   (c) Uses many unusual words to create striking description.
   (d) Implies his message subtly rather than stating it clearly.   ____   ____

USING THE WORDS

(1) Words and Their Meanings: Find the boldfaced word for these definitions.

   _____   (a) regain courage or strength

   _____   (b) a temporary army encampment

   _____   (c) serious, determined, eager

   _____   (d) a now mainly poetic term for verses or metrical units

_____ (e) fated, determined beforehand, as by divine will

_____ (f) wrapped up in order to deaden or dull sound

_____ (g) elevated and noble

_____ (h) deserted, forsaken

(2) Write a paragraph using four of the words from the list above. Use a separate piece of paper.

WRITING ABOUT IT

Use a separate piece of paper.

(1) What is Longfellow's concept of life? Do you think it differs from people's concept of life today? Do you agree with his concept? Answer these questions, giving specific examples to illustrate your views.

(2) Longfellow talks about doing things we can be remembered for. Describe the things you would like to achieve during your life and be remembered for.

THE DROUGHT

ABOUT THE PASSAGE

In *The Grapes of Wrath*, John Steinbeck tells about the terrible drought of the 1930's that caused hundreds of small farmers to leave the land. Notice how he cleverly establishes the situation and atmosphere in this opening chapter.

REASON FOR READING

To see how Steinbeck effectively describes the devastation that the drought has brought to the land. Which word does he use repeatedly? What does it symbolize? What does he refer to, to show the progressive destruction of the drought?

READ THE PASSAGE

To the red country and part of the gray country of Oklahoma, the last rains came gently, and they did not cut the scarred earth. The plows crossed and recrossed the **rivulet** marks. The last rains lifted the corn quickly and scattered weed colonies and grass along the sides of the roads so that the gray country and the dark red country began to disappear under a green cover. In the last part of May the sky grew pale and the clouds that had hung in high puffs for so long in the spring were **dissipated.** The sun flared down on the growing corn day after day until a line of brown spread along the edge of each green bayonet. The clouds appeared, and went away, and in a while they did not try any more. The weeds grew darker green to protect themselves, and they did not spread any more. The surface of the earth crusted, a thin hard crust, and as the sky became pale, so the earth became pale, pink in the red country and white in the gray country.

In the water-cut gullies the earth dusted down in dry little streams. Gophers and ant lions started small avalanches. And as the sharp sun struck day after day, the leaves of the young corn became less stiff and erect; they bent in a curve at first, and then, as the central ribs of strength grew weak, each leaf tilted downward. Then it was June and the sun shone more fiercely. The brown lines on the corn leaves widened and moved in on the central ribs. The weeds frayed and edged back toward their roots. The air was thin and the sky more pale; and every day the earth paled.

In the roads where the teams moved, where the wheels **milled** the ground and the hooves of the horses beat the ground, the dirt crust broke and the dust formed. Every moving thing lifted the dust into the air: a walking man lifted a thin layer as high as his waist, and a wagon lifted the dust as high as the fence tops, and an automobile boiled a cloud behind it. The dust was long in settling back again.

When June was half gone, the big clouds moved up out of Texas and the Gulf, high heavy clouds, rain-heads. The men in the fields looked up at the clouds and sniffed at them and held wet fingers up to sense the wind. And the horses were nervous while the clouds were up. The rain-heads dropped a little spattering and hurried on to some other country. Behind them the sky was pale again and the sun flared. In the dust there were drop craters where the rain had fallen, and there were clean splashes on the corn, and that was all.

A gentle wind followed the rain clouds, driving them on northward, a wind that softly clashed the drying corn. A day went by and the wind increased, steady, unbroken by gusts. The dust from the roads fluffed up and spread out and fell on the weeds beside the fields, and fell into the fields a little way. Now the wind grew strong and hard and it worked at the rain crust in the corn fields. Little by little the sky was darkened by the mixing dust, and the wind felt over the earth, loosened the dust, and carried it away. The wind grew stronger. The rain crust broke and the dust lifted up out of the fields and drove gray **plumes** into the air like **sluggish** smoke. The corn threshed the wind and made a dry, rushing sound. The finest dust did not settle back to earth now, but disappeared into the darkening sky.

The wind grew stronger, whisked under stones, carried up straws and old leaves, and even little clods, marking its course as it sailed across the fields. The air and the sky darkened and through them the sun shone redly, and there was a raw **sting** in the air. During the night the wind raced faster over the land, dug cunningly among the rootlets of the corn, and the corn fought the wind with its weakened leaves until the roots were freed by the prying wind and then each stalk settled wearily sideways toward the earth and pointed the direction of the wind.

The dawn came, but no day. In the gray sky a red sun appeared, a dim red circle that gave a little light, like dusk; and as that day advanced, the dusk slipped back toward darkness, and the wind cried and whimpered over the fallen corn.

Men and women huddled in their houses, and they tied handkerchiefs over their noses when they went out, and wore goggles to protect their eyes.

When the night came again it was black night, for the stars could not pierce the dust to get down, and the window lights could not even spread beyond their own yards. Now the dust was evenly mixed with the air, an **emulsion** of dust and air. Houses were shut tight, and cloth wedged around doors and windows, but the dust came in so thinly that it could not be seen in the air, and it settled like pollen on the chairs and tables, on the dishes. The people brushed it from their shoulders. Little lines of dust lay at the door sills.

In the middle of that night the wind passed on and left the land quiet. The dust-filled air muffled sound more completely than fog does. The people, lying in their beds, heard the wind stop. They awakened when the rushing wind was gone. They lay quietly and listened deep into the stillness. Then the roosters crowed, and their voices were muffled, and the people stirred restlessly in their beds and wanted the morning. They knew it would take a long time for the dust to settle out of the air. In the morning the dust hung like fog, and the sun was as red as ripe new blood. All day the dust sifted down from the sky, and the next day it sifted down. An even blanket covered the earth. It settled on the corn, piled up on the tops of the fence posts, piled up on the wires; it settled on roofs, **blanketed** the weeds and trees.

THINKING IT OVER

(1) Which word does Steinbeck use repeatedly? _____

What does it symbolize? _____

_____

(2) Did you notice that Steinbeck uses color to show the progressive destruction of the drought? Tell how the

colors change: _____

_____

(3) In which state is the drought? _____

STUDYING THE PASSAGE

(1) Find the Main Idea: Choose one.
    (a) The changing color of the landscape.
    (b) Life without rain.
    (c) How dusty everything is.
    (d) The effect of the drought on the land. _____

(2) Find the Facts: Mark each one *true* or *false*.
  (a) A heavy storm brought the last rain. _____
  (b) The weeds became darker green due to the lack of rain. _____
  (c) Every day the earth became paler. _____
  (d) The wind became increasingly strong. _____
  (e) The wind was helpful as it blew the dust away. _____
  (f) The daytime seemed like nighttime. _____
  (g) The dust made everything quiet. _____
  (h) The dust hid the sun. _____

(3) Find the Order: Number the following in the order in which they appear in the passage.
  (a) A gentle wind followed the rainclouds, driving them on northward. _____
  (b) They lay quietly and listened deep into the stillness. _____
  (c) In the last part of May the sky grew pale. _____
  (d) An even blanket covered the earth. _____
  (e) In the water-cut gullies the earth dusted down in dry little streams. _____
  (f) During the night the wind raced faster over the land. _____
  (g) Every moving thing lifted dust into the air. _____
  (h) Men and women huddled in their houses. _____

(4) Go beyond the Facts: From reading Steinbeck's introduction, and realizing his description of the drought's destruction of the land is also symbolic, which two of the following are themes of *The Grapes of Wrath*?
  (a) The problem of survival.
  (b) The threatened loss of human dignity and loss of morale.
  (c) The idea that all people are equal.
  (d) Everyone should have a dream. _____ _____

(5) Determine the Writer's Style and Technique: Which one of the following is *not* true of Steinbeck's writing style?
  (a) Highly descriptive.
  (b) Exquisite attention to detail.
  (c) Verbose—too wordy.
  (d) Use of symbolism. _____

USING THE WORDS

(1) Words and Their Meanings: Find the boldfaced word for these definitions.

_____ (a) covered

_____ (b) a mixture of liquids (usually) in which very fine drops of one are evenly scattered throughout the other

_____ (c) a little stream, brook

_____ (d) like fluffy feathers

_____ (e) slow-moving, like a slug

_____ (f) broke up and disappeared

63

_____ (g) ridged; ground up like grain

_____ (h) to cause or feel sharp pain

(2) Write a paragraph using four of the words from the list above. Use a separate piece of paper.

WRITING ABOUT IT

Use a separate piece of paper.

(1) Write a review, or analysis, of Steinbeck's writing. Explain how his choice of words is imaginative and effective. Think about the aspects of nature Steinbeck writes about so powerfully, such as dust, wind, and color changes. What do they symbolize? How does the author show this? Tell why his writing would be less effective if it were less detailed. Then discuss how the entire chapter slowly builds up an oppressive atmosphere.

(2) Try your hand at writing a descriptive passage. Drawing upon what you have learned by reading and analyzing Steinbeck's writing, describe the effect on the land of a relentless rainstorm. Give as explicit details as you can; appeal to the reader's visual and auditory senses; include symbolism if you think you can use it effectively; and create a certain mood.

MONKEYING AROUND WITH MATH*

ABOUT THE PASSAGE   If you don't like arithmetic, you might love the beauty of math, says the
writer of this passage. What does he mean?

REASON FOR READING   To follow two logical explanations:
(1) Why the writer loves mathematics.
(2) How a mathematical problem is solved.

READ THE PASSAGE

If you are among those who find arithmetic **tedious** and boring, frankly, I agree with you. So do most mathematicians. Real math is a lot more than arithmetic and vastly more interesting than doing endless calculations. I was lucky enough to learn that as a youngster and ever since I have been fascinated with the subject.

I want to encourage you to share in this pleasure. I realize that some people will remain hostile or indifferent to mathematics; nobody says all of us must share enthusiasms. But because I believe that mathematics is one of the supreme achievements of the human species, I'd like you to glimpse its pleasures.

I hope to convince some readers that pursuit of math can offer rewards akin to pleasures that come from the music of Ellington or Schubert, the choreography of Balanchine or Ailey, the painting of Monet or [Winslow] Homer, the drama of Shakespeare or Beckett, the architecture of Wright or Sullivan.

Finally, I hope to attain this goal with a simple example clear to anyone who can add, subtract, multiply and divide. Nothing is required beyond willingness to follow my guided tour of the example, which we'll see in a minute.

Let me start by explaining what mathematicians see as the **essence** of their field. Based on depressing early experience or hearsay, many people think that mathematics invariably involves long, complex, **prodigiously** tedious calculations based on seemingly **arbitrary** rules. In fact, most mathematicians find that sort of thing just as boring as anyone else. They are driven by something quite different—discovering the beauty revealed in the ways that numbers relate to one another, the unveiling of another of nature's "secrets."

The most helpful definition of mathematics is that it is the science of form and pattern, and isn't that what much of art is about? Mathematics starts with particular instances involving numbers—say, 2 plus 2 equals 4—and goes on to seek patterns that govern whole classes of comparable cases. How? By observing similar examples, monkeying with them (yes, "monkeying," there is no better term for it) and by the mysterious surprise of insight.

Once you suspect a pattern, you use it on other examples and, if the testing goes well, you establish the pattern as a "law" with a formal logical proof. Then, instead of having to work out each similar problem in detail, you can take advantage of the overall pattern to determine answers with the least labor.

Thus, the basic activity of mathematics is generalizing from the particular to the general, not so much to save work as to strive for the simplest and therefore most elegant ways to express relationships among quantities. The primary reward of such activity, as in art, is to glimpse the beauty of patterns that are revealed. Albert Einstein once put it this way in the *New York Times*:

"Pure mathematics is, in its way, the poetry of logical ideas. One seeks the most general ideas of

*"The Beauty of Mathematics," by Alan M. Kriegsman, © March 13, 1996, *The Washington Post*. Reprinted with permission.

operation which will bring together in simple, logical and unified form the largest possible circle of formal relationships. In this effort toward logical beauty, spiritual formulas are discovered necessary for the deeper penetration into the laws of nature."

Now to my example. It's an old, old part of mathematical **lore,** but I did have the joy of discovering it on my own before I knew that others had preceded me. No doubt many others have experienced the same thrill of discovery.

Suppose you want to add up all whole numbers (no fractions) from 1 to 100. You could take the "brute force" approach by adding 1 and 2, the first case at hand, and getting 3, then adding 3, the next number, to this result and getting 6. You could do this until you come to the final number, 100, and you'd have the correct answer after 99 steps.

But who wants to do all that work?

Here the art of mathematics comes into play, as opposed to **raw** calculation. A real mathematician would seek a simpler method of adding the numbers from 1 to 100. Can we discover some relationship among numbers that will show us the way?

As the real math begins, its explanation lies beyond the realm of the rational. It remains a profound mystery. The next step involves experimentation—"monkeying around"—observation and, most crucially, insight. All humans have some aptitude for insight, for mathematical understanding. Of course, this talent varies with individuals because we all aren't born to be Einsteins. But history and anthropology teach that this aptitude is universal, like the ability to learn a language.

One way to approach a problem, often invoked by practicing mathematicians, is to simplify it. Instead of asking for the sum of numbers from 1 to 100, we can reduce the problem, for instance, to the numbers from 1 to 3, obviously an easier challenge, and seek a workable system.

One plus 2 equals 3; adding the next number in the series, 3, to this result equals 6, and that is our answer. So far, we have gotten exactly nowhere. This still is the "brute force" method.

But after considerable fiddling around, which mathematicians spend much time doing, you might notice this: If you were to write the numbers 1 + 2 + 3 = 6 and then reverse the order underneath, you would have:

$$1 + 2 + 3 = 6$$
$$3 + 2 + 1 = 6$$

You would notice that it doesn't matter in which order you add the numbers.

Then, monkeying further, you might think to add the numbers in each column. You would notice quickly that in each case (1 + 3, 2 + 2 and 3 + 1), you get a remarkable result, the same answer each time—4.

It would look like this:

$$1 + 2 + 3 = 6$$
$$\underline{3 + 2 + 1 = 6}$$
$$4 + 4 + 4 = 12$$

Could this **consistency** be a clue?

Math can be like that.

Since there are three instances in which you did an addition problem, you might think to multiply the 4 by the 3 instances and get 12.

Is 12 any closer to what you know is the correct answer to adding 1, 2 and 3 because you simplified the problem? You might notice that it is exactly double the correct answer.

Taking another leap of mathematical **intuition,** you might ask whether you have stumbled on another possibility—divide the number in half.

By another means, we now have the same answer we obtained by "brute force."

So far, it may not seem like progress. Worse yet, we have converted a problem of addition into one requiring multiplication and division.

Maybe we have hit on something, or maybe our roundabout method is too simple or just plain wrong. How could we be sure? One obvious way would be to test the method on other problems.

Try adding the numbers from 1 to 4, or 1 to 5 or 1 to 17. You'll see that the pattern holds in all of these cases.

What has been gained by our new method? In our test case, we made more work for ourselves. But here the beauty of the new method reveals itself. Remember our original problem, adding all whole numbers from 1 to 100? As we saw previously, the "brute force" method requires 99 steps. But the new method requires the same three steps.

To add the numbers from 1 to 100 using the new method requires only these operations: add the first number (1) to the last (100), equalling 101, and multiply that by the number of instances involved (100), giving us 10,100. Divide this by 2, and 5,050 is the correct answer. We have cut our labor from 99 steps to three.

Let's look even more closely. The three-step method applies to all similar cases. Say you want to add whole numbers from 1 to 10,000,000. The "brute force" method would require one less than 10 million steps, but our newfound method produces the correct answer in the same three steps.

Add the first number to the last, multiply by the number of instances (in this case 10 million) and halve the result. The possibilities in terms of number are endless. The beauty isn't merely in reducing the workload but in discovering a pattern applicable to all whole numbers.

In formal math, only one step remains—writing our discovery in a formula that anybody can use. For example, mathematicians would label the last number in a sequence to be added as the abstract n. In those terms, our new method would become this:

Step one: Add the first number in the sequence, namely, 1, to the last such number, n. Write that as $n + 1$.

Step two: Multiply $n + 1$ by the number of instances, which is always equal to the last number. That's n. Write that as $n(n+1)$.

Step three: Halve the result. That would be written:

$$\frac{n(n + 1)}{2}$$

There you have it. No matter how large "n," the formula works. We have discovered a pattern in an ordinary sequence of numbers.

Mathematicians have generalized this very method to cover other sequences of additions, for example, adding all the odd numbers from 3 to 1,003. This is where the beauty of a mathematical, rather than a calculational, approach arises—in the key step of insight, discovery of an unsuspected pattern based on somewhat random experimentation. This was a simple example, but it shows principles that apply to all of mathematics even in its most advanced reaches.

If the existence of this pattern intrigues you, if discovering it makes you feel that you have glimpsed something fundamental about numbers, you've tasted one of the pleasures of real mathematics. And I have succeeded.

THINKING IT OVER

(1) What does the writer say is the most helpful definition of mathematics? _____

_____

(2) What is the basic activity of mathematics? _____

_____

_____

(3) What does "monkeying around" with math involve? _____

_____

STUDYING THE PASSAGE

(1) Find the Main Idea: Choose one.
   (a) Solving math problems takes only three steps.
   (b) How to solve math problems.
   (c) Math is an art.
   (d) The pleasures of mathematics.   _____

(2) Find the Facts: Mark each one *true* or *false*.
   (a) The writer thinks everyone likes mathematics.   _____
   (b) The writer believes mathematics is similar to art.   _____
   (c) The key to solving math problems is to find a pattern.   _____
   (d) Einstein said, "Pure mathematics is the poetry of logical ideas."   _____
   (e) In the "brute force" method of solving math problems you systematically go through each step of the calculations.   _____
   (f) Adding the numbers 1 to 100 would take 99 steps by the "brute force" method.   _____
   (g) One way to test a method is to apply it to other problems.   _____
   (h) The formula for adding numbers can be written as $\underline{n(n+1)}$.
                                        2   _____

(3) Find the Order: Number the following in the order in which they appear in the passage.
   (a) But who wants to do all that work?   _____
   (b) If you were to write the numbers 1 + 2 + 3 = 6 and then reverse the order underneath . . .   _____
   (c) Mathematics starts with particular instances involving numbers—say, 2 plus 2 equals 4.   _____
   (d) Divide this by 2, and 5,050 is the correct answer.   _____
   (e) Instead of asking for the sum of numbers from 1 to 100, we can reduce the problem.   _____
   (f) Real math is a lot more than arithmetic.   _____
   (g) No matter how large "n," the formula works.   _____
   (h) I hope to attain this goal with a simple example clear to anyone who can add, subtract, multiply and divide.   _____

(4) Go beyond the Facts: If the writer had been a mathematics teacher (he is a journalist) which of the following methods would he probably *not* have used to teach mathematics?
   (a) Given a lot of math problems to the students for them to solve each day.
   (b) Taught the broad underlying concepts of math and have the students apply them to new problems.
   (c) Had the students formulate their own concepts and experiment by trial and error.
   (d) Had the students discuss the math problems in class rather than memorize math "rules."   _____

(5) Determine the Writer's Style and Technique: The writer's intention in the article is to convince the reader that pleasure can be found in mathematics. Which *two* of the following does he do to convince the reader?
   (a) He gives a logical explanation of why he finds pleasure in mathematics.
   (b) He tries to prove his point by giving one specific math problem.
   (c) He tries to prove his point by giving various, different math problems.
   (d) He shows how useful math can be in one's daily life.   _____   _____

USING THE WORDS

(1) Words and Their Meanings: Find the boldfaced word for these definitions.

_____ (a) a way of knowing something without actually thinking it out or studying; instant understanding

_____ (b) based only on what one wants or thinks; ignoring rules or others' opinions

_____ (c) knowledge or learning, especially that handed down from earlier times

_____ (d) very great, huge, enormous

_____ (e) unrefined

_____ (f) that which makes something what it is; the most important or basic quality of a thing

_____ (g) acting or thinking always in the same way

_____ (h) long and boring

(2) Write a paragraph using four of the words from the list above. Use a separate piece of paper.

WRITING ABOUT IT

Use a separate piece of paper.

(1) Did you understand the explanation of the math problem? If you did not, reread the passage. Then, without referring to the passage, see if you can explain the three-step approach used to add the numbers 1 to 100. Include in your explanation the steps the writer took to formulate his three-step approach.

(2) You have read the writer's views on the subject of mathematics. Now give your views. Say whether you like math or not. Substantiate your viewpoint with specific examples. Include such aspects as: how math is taught to you; whether you find math easy or hard; the application you see, or don't see, of the math you learn in class to your daily living; and generally how you feel about math.

THE MATH OF CHAIN LETTERS

ABOUT THE PASSAGE   Have you ever received a chain letter? Did you send it on, together with the other copies you were instructed to send? Does everyone do this? How does the writer of this passage know that this is not so?

REASON FOR READING   To follow a mathematical explanation that shows that the chain letter's instructions are impossible.

READ THE PASSAGE

"With love all things are possible. This paper has been sent to you for good luck. The original is in New England. It has been around the world nine times. You will receive good luck within four days of receiving this letter provided you, in turn, send it on. . . . Please send 20 copies and see what happens in four days."

Chances are you've received a "chain letter" like this, perhaps from a well-meaning friend. You may even have been tempted to forward it. The copy I received came with a cover note saying, "For obvious reasons, I wouldn't dare not pass it on." But I know that the vast majority of recipients have ignored the instructions.

How do I know? If everyone had followed the law of the letter, you and I and the rest of the world would be buried in copies. The math isn't hard to figure.

Consider, for instance, that 20 copies of the letter are to be sent out within four days of receipt. So, on the first mailing, 20 copies hit the street. Four days later, each of those 20 recipients sends copies to 20 "friends" providing a wave of mail consisting of 20 x 20 = 400 pieces. The chart below shows what happens for the next month:

Mailing	Day	Number of Copies
1	1	20
2	4	$20 \times 20 = 400$
3	8	$20 \times 20 \times 20 = 8,000$
4	12	$20^4 = 160,000$
5	16	$20^5 = 3.2$ million
6	20	$20^6 = 64$ million
7	24	$20^7 = 1.3$ billion
8	28	$20^8 = 26$ billion copies!

The world's population is about 5.5 billion. In less than a month, this chain letter should have produced copies in **quintuplicate** for every man, woman and child on Earth. That wouldn't bury all of us, but read on.

The letter I received claims that someone named Constantine Dias received a copy 42 years ago. Dias supposedly passed on 20 copies and promptly won a 2 million lottery. The 42-year period represents 15,430 days or 3,835 waves of mailing. Had the chain remained unbroken, the last ripple of the wave would consist of 20^{3835} pieces for the Postal Service to shoulder.

That's more than my calculator can compute, but a little approximation puts the grand total at more than 10^{4500}. In other words, more than a 1 followed by 4,500 zeroes. "Bulk mail" indeed!

It's hard to conceive of numbers so large, especially since the known stars in the sky number only about 10^{22}. If this chain letter were truly unbroken, it would have produced more letters than there are atoms in the known universe—a mere 10^{79}, give or take a few zillion.

We can make a few **crude** guesses as to how many folks are **perpetuating** the letter. For the last few years, I've seen some version of this particular letter about twice a year.

Taking my personal experience at **face value,** sometimes a bad idea, we might guess that the total number of chain letters in the mail is about constant. If the number of copies in circulation were really increasing in a chain reaction, the number reaching me should grow rapidly from year to year.

"Chain Letters and Pyramid Schemes," by Chip Denman, © February 14, 1996, *The Washington Post*. Reprinted with permission.

The steady rate that I see would happen if one of every 20 recipients followed the letter's instructions while the other 19 tossed it in the recycling bin.

How many copies in circulation does this mean? We can determine that if we assume that my twice-a-year experience is typical.

We could multiply the chances of getting this chain letter on a given day of the year (2 out of 365 or 2/365) times the number of people able to use the mail, say 150 million of the 250 million people in the United States. Do the math, and you have about 820,000 recipients on any given day.

Thus it looks as if 41,000 people, less than .02 percent of the U.S. population, generating 20 fresh copies daily, could account for the volume I'm seeing.

This particular letter is basically **innocuous.** It doesn't ask us to send money or even to believe in superstitions. All we have to do is copy and mail it and wait for good stuff to happen. "This is true even if you are not superstitious," it promises. It is no more **pernicious** than the newspaper's daily horoscope and few people would let it run their lives.

New technologies offer new opportunities. Electronic mail makes it even easier for otherwise rational folks to indulge their superstitions. A few keystrokes and that letter has been copied and forwarded to 20 cybervictims.

Even without stamps to lick, the math still holds. There aren't enough electrons in the universe to support this mass behavior. Even on a small scale, such electronic mailings consume limited resources, slow other mail traffic and generally waste "bandwidth."

Similar poor appreciation of math lies behind much more costly and **insidious** schemes. Some chain letters try to sucker dupes into sending money to the head of a pyramid in the hope that eventually, if the chain remains unbroken, the lucky players will more than recoup their stake as they reach the top and collect cash from new players.

A small-scale version a few years ago suggested building a music library by sending compact discs rather than cash, but it shared the same shaky pyramid structure. The Postal Service considers such schemes illegal games of chance and will prosecute for mail fraud. If you receive such a letter, postal authorities ask that you contact your postmaster.

Similar bad math underlies pyramid investment schemes. A recent example is the collapse of the Foundation for New Era Philanthropy last spring. Hundreds of nonprofit and charitable organizations, including a Boy Scout troop in Pennsylvania and a group providing **mentors** for disadvantaged youths in the District of Columbia, bought into this plan.

New Era promised a 100 percent return within six months but, unknown to investors, was a pyramid that depended on new waves of investors to pay their predecessors.

The earliest investors saw their hopes come true. But in all such schemes, eventually there are fewer new participants, and the chain is broken. Those who join late lose their upfront investment.

This kind of chain is called a Ponzi scheme, in dubious honor of Charles Ponzi, who made and lost fortunes in Boston in 1919.

Such "Pyramid power" is about as likely to bring you luck and wealth as any other kind of magic charm—that is to say, not at all.

THINKING IT OVER

(1) How does the writer know that not everyone follows the instructions of the chain letter they receive?

_____

(2) How many people out of 20 does the writer think respond to a chain letter? _____

_____

(3) Now that we have electronic mail, will it be possible for everyone to follow the instructions of a chain letter?

_____

_____

STUDYING THE PASSAGE

(1) Find the Main Idea: Choose one.
    (a) Why you should not respond to chain letters.
    (b) How to respond to chain letters.
    (c) The impossibility of chain letters being perpetuated.
    (d) Why it is easier to send chain letters through electronic mail.   _____

(2) Find the Facts: Mark each one *true* or *false*.
    (a) If everyone followed the instructions of the chain letter, after 4 days 400 letters
        would have been mailed.   _____
    (b) After 12 days 8,000 letters would have been sent.   _____
    (c) After 28 days 26 billion copies would have been sent.   _____
    (d) In less than a month everyone on Earth could have received 5 copies.   _____
    (e) If the chain letter had been truly unbroken, it would have produced more letters
        than there are atoms in the universe.   _____
    (f) The writer estimates 41,000 people are sending the 20 letters annually.   _____
    (g) Some investment schemes are based on the chain letter theory.   _____
    (h) It is inevitable that these pyramid schemes will fail.   _____

(3) Find the Order: Number the following in the order in which they appear in the passage.
    (a) The chart below shows what happens for the next month.   _____
    (b) We can make a few crude guesses as to how many folks actually are perpetuating
        the letter.   _____
    (c) This kind of chain is called the Ponzi scheme.   _____
    (d) This particular letter is basically innocuous.   _____
    (e) It has been around the world nine times.   _____
    (f) Some chain letters try to sucker dupes into sending money.   _____
    (g) You and I and the rest of the world would be buried in copies.   _____
    (h) The 42-year period represents 15,430 days or 3,835 waves of mailing.   _____

(4) Go beyond the Facts: Which of the following could be assumed from the passage? The people who start
    chains most likely:
    (a) Do it to gain something for themselves.
    (b) Do it because they want to help others.
    (c) Do it because they enjoy contacting people.
    (d) Do it because they enjoy annoying people.   _____

(5) Determine the Writer's Style and Technique: Which of the following does the writer *not* do?
    (a) Relate a personal experience.
    (b) Use mathematical calculations to prove a point.
    (c) Use a chart as a visual aid.
    (d) Make a comparison.   _____

USING THE WORDS

(1) Words and Their Meanings: Find the boldfaced word for these definitions.

_____   (a) harmless

_____   (b) rough; unrefined; lacking manners or grace

_____   (c) dishonest, sly, or tricky; more dangerous than it seems to be

_____   (d) wise, loyal advisers; teachers or coaches

_____   (e) causing to be continued or remembered

_____   (f) causing great injury, harm, damage

_____   (g) five times over

_____   (h) as it appears on the surface

(2) Write a paragraph using four of the words from the list above. Use a separate piece of paper.

WRITING ABOUT IT

Use a separate piece of paper.

(1) Write a letter to a friend dissuading him or her from investing in a pyramid scheme. Explain the mathematics behind your advice.

(2) The chain letter said the recipient would receive good luck within four days of receiving the letter. Imagine this came true in the form of a day full of good luck. Describe the day.

A LOVE STORY*

ABOUT THE PASSAGE This story may have helped inspire Shakespeare's *Romeo and Juliet*, which in turn was the inspiration for Leonard Bernstein's musical, *West Side Story*. If you know these stories, you know what happens to the two people in love in this story.

REASON FOR READING To read this old myth, which was first told by the Latin poet Ovid, and to find out why mulberry bushes now have red berries.

READ THE PASSAGE

Once upon a time the deep red berries of the mulberry tree were white as snow. The change in color came about strangely and sadly. The death of two young lovers was the cause.

Pyramus and Thisbe, he the most beautiful youth and she the loveliest maiden of all the East, lived in Babylon, the city of Queen Semiramis, in houses so close together that one wall was common to both. Growing up thus side by side they learned to love each other. They longed to marry, but their parents forbade. Love, however, cannot be forbidden. The more that flame is covered up, the hotter it burns. Also love can always find a way. It was impossible that these two whose hearts were on fire should be kept apart.

In the wall both houses shared there was a little **chink.** No one before had noticed it, but there is nothing a lover does not notice. Our two young people discovered it and through it they were able to whisper sweetly back and forth, Thisbe on one side, Pyramus on the other. The **hateful** wall that separated them had become their means of reaching each other. "But for you we could touch, kiss," they would say. "But at least you let us speak together. You give a passage for loving words to reach loving ears. We are not ungrateful." So they would talk, and as night came on and they must part, each would press on the wall kisses that could not go through to the lips on the other side.

Every morning when the dawn had put out the stars, and the sun's rays had dried the **hoarfrost** on the grass, they would steal to the crack and, standing there, now utter words of burning love and now **lament** their hard fate, but always in softest whispers. Finally a day came when they could endure no longer. They decided that that very night they would try to slip away and steal out through the city into the open country where at last they could be together in freedom. They agreed to meet at a well-known place, the Tomb of Ninus, under a tree there, a tall mulberry full of snow-white berries, near which a cool spring bubbled up. The plan pleased them and it seemed to them the day would never end.

At last the sun sank into the sea and night arose. In the darkness Thisbe crept out and made her way in all secrecy to the tomb. Pyramus had not come; still she waited for him, her love making her **bold.** But of a sudden she saw by the light of the moon a lioness. The **fierce** beast had made a kill; her jaws were bloody and she was coming to slake her thirst in the spring. She was still far enough away for Thisbe to escape, but as she fled she dropped her cloak. The lioness came upon it on her way back to her lair and she mouthed it and tore it before disappearing into the woods. That is what Pyramus saw when he appeared a few minutes later. Before him lay the bloodstained shreds of the cloak and clear in the dust were the tracks of the lioness. The conclusion was **inevitable.** He never doubted that he knew all. Thisbe was dead. He had let his love, a tender maiden, come alone to a place full of danger, and not been there first to protect her. "It is I who killed you," he said. He lifted up from the trampled dust what was left of the cloak and kissing it again and again, carried it to the mulberry tree. "Now," he said. "you shall drink my blood too." He drew his sword and plunged it into his side. The blood spurted up over the berries and dyed them a dark red.

Thisbe, although terrified of the lioness, was still more afraid to fail her lover. She ventured to go back to the tree of the **tryst,** the mulberry with the shining white fruit. She could not find it. A tree was there, but not one gleam of white was on the branches. As she stared at it, something moved on the ground beneath. She started back shuddering. But in a moment, peering through the shadows, she saw what was there. It was Pyramus, bathed in blood and dying. She flew to him and threw her arms around him. She kissed his cold lips and begged him to look at her, to speak to her. "It is I, your Thisbe, your dearest," she cried to him. At the sound of her name he opened his heavy eyes for one look. Then death closed them.

She saw his sword fallen from his hand and beside it her cloak stained and torn. She understood all. "Your own hand killed you," she said, "and your love for me. I too can be brave. I too can love. Only death would have had the power to separate us. It shall not have that power now." She plunged into her heart the sword that was still wet with his life's blood.

The gods were pitiful at the end, and the lovers' parents too. The deep red fruit of the mulberry is the everlasting memorial of these true lovers, and one urn holds the ashes of the two whom not even death could part.

THINKING IT OVER

(1) What color were the berries on the mulberry tree originally? _____

How did they change color? _____

_____

(2) What did the lovers do when they parted each night? _____

_____

(3) Where did the lovers arrange to meet? _____

_____

STUDYING THE PASSAGE

(1) Find the Main Idea: Choose one.
    (a) The death of two lovers.
    (b) How a misunderstanding led to the death of two lovers.
    (c) Why two people gave their lives for each other.
    (d) The consequences of being too much in love.   _____

(2) Find the Facts: Mark each one *true* or *false*.
    (a) Pyramus and Thisbe lived in ancient Rome.   _____
    (b) Their yards were separated by a wall.   _____
    (c) The couple hated, yet loved, the wall.   _____
    (d) The young lovers planned their meeting several months in advance.   _____
    (e) Thisbe saw a lioness with bloody jaws.   _____

(f) The lioness pulled off Thisbe's cloak.   _____

(g) Pyramus blamed himself for what he thought was Thisbe's death.   _____

(h) Pyramus saw Thisbe was alive before he died.   _____

(3) Find the Order: Number the following in the order in which they appear in the passage.

  (a) Still she waited for him, her love making her bold.   _____

  (b) They longed to marry, but their parents forbade.   _____

  (c) As she stared at it, something moved on the ground beneath.   _____

  (d) They would steal to the crack and, standing there, now utter words of burning love. _____

  (e) She understood all.   _____

  (f) Before him lay the bloodstained shreds of the cloak.   _____

  (g) "But for you we could touch, kiss," they would say.   _____

  (h) They agreed to meet at a well-known place.   _____

(4) Go beyond the Facts: The writer insinuates that the couple's love became greater for which reasons? Choose two.

  (a) When you are not allowed to do something, you want to do it even more.

  (b) Each saw the other one becoming even more beautiful and handsome.

  (c) They did not have any other friends their own age.

  (d) Their clandestine contacts at the wall gave them a sense of risk and romance.   _____   _____

(5) Determine the Writer's Style and Technique: Which one of the following does the writer *not* do?

  (a) Tell the story in a very matter of fact, straightforward way.

  (b) Tell the story very dramatically.

  (c) Use very descriptive language.

  (d) Describe the characters' innermost thoughts.   _____

USING THE WORDS

(1) Words and Their Meanings: Find the boldfaced word for these definitions.

_____   (a) intrepid, audacious

_____   (b) obnoxious, abhorrent, odious

_____   (c) truculent, bellicose, vehement

_____   (d) a narrow opening; crack

_____   (e) an appointment to meet at a certain time and place, usually a secret, romantic meeting

_____   (f) white, frozen dew

_____   (g) unavoidable

_____   (h) to feel or show deep sorrow over something

(2) Write a paragraph using four of the words from the list above. Use a separate piece of paper.

WRITING ABOUT IT

Use a separate piece of paper.

(1) Write a story about two people in love who are forbidden to see each other. Explain how they contact one another, how and where they meet, and what happens to them in the end.

(2) Pyramus and Thisbe would not have met their gory end if their parents had let them see one another. Do you think parents should have a say in deciding who their teenagers go out with? Should they check to see if the friend is "acceptable"? Should they concern themselves with their teenager's dating and specify how often they can date? Is a curfew appropriate? Give your opinion on this topic, including specific reasons and examples to illustrate your views.

THE RAVEN*

ABOUT THE PASSAGE

This poem is about a student whose lover has recently died. One bleak December evening, while studying, he hears a raven tapping at his window. The raven enters, and they have a long conversation, though the raven offers only one-word comments.

REASON FOR READING

Poe created "The Raven" to achieve an effect of mournful, eternal remembrance of his loved one. Notice how he does this through the skillful use of phonetics (the sounds of the words) and descriptive wording; symbolism; and the story of a young man despairing for his lover.

    The poem is divided into three parts. See if you can identify which stanzas make up each part. The first part introduces the student and the situation, and the arrival of the raven. The second part becomes more serious as the conversation between the student and the raven intensifies. The final part summarizes the central theme of the poem.

1

Once upon a midnight dreary, while I pondered, weak and weary,
Over many a quaint and curious volume of forgotten lore—
While I nodded, nearly napping, suddenly there came a tapping,
As of some one gently rapping, rapping at my chamber door.
" 'Tis some visiter," I muttered, "tapping at my chamber door—
              Only this and nothing more."

2

Ah, distinctly I remember it was in the bleak December,
And each separate dying ember wrought its ghost upon the floor.
Eagerly I wished the morrow;—vainly I had sought to borrow
From my books **surcease** of sorrow—sorrow for the lost Lenore—
For the rare and radiant maiden whom the angels name Lenore—
              Nameless *here* for evermore.

3

And the silken, sad, uncertain rustling of each purple curtain
Thrilled me—filled me with fantastic terrors never felt before;
So that now, to still the beating of my heart, I stood repeating:
" 'Tis some visiter entreating entrance at my chamber door—
Some late visiter entreating entrance at my chamber door;
              This it is and nothing more."

4

Presently my soul grew stronger; hesitating then no longer,
"Sir," said I, "or Madam, truly your forgiveness I implore;
But the fact is I was napping, and so gently you came rapping,
And so faintly you came tapping, tapping at my chamber door,
That I scarce was sure I heard you"—here I opened wide the door;—
              Darkness there and nothing more.

* "The Raven" by Edgar Allan Poe.

Deep into that darkness peering, long I stood there, wondering, fearing,
Doubting, dreaming dreams no mortal ever dared to dream before;

5 But the silence was unbroken, and the stillness gave no token,
And the only word there spoken was the whispered word, "Lenore?"
This I whispered, and an echo murmured back the word "Lenore!"
>> Merely this and nothing more.

Back into the chamber turning, all my soul within me burning,
Soon again I heard a tapping somewhat louder than before.

6 "Surely," said I, "surely that is something at my window lattice;
Let me see, then, what thereat is, and this mystery explore,—
Let my heart be still a moment and this mystery explore,—
>> 'Tis the wind and nothing more!"

Open here I flung the shutter, when, with many a flirt and flutter,
In there stepped a stately Raven of the saintly days of yore;

7 Not the least **obeisance** made he; not a minute stopped or stayed he;
But with mien of lord or lady, perched above my chamber door—
Perched upon a bust of Pallas just above my chamber door—
>> Perched, and sat, and nothing more.

Then this ebony bird beguiling my sad fancy into smiling,
By the grave and stern **decorum** of the countenance it wore,

8 "Though thy crest be shorn and shaven, thou," I said, "art sure no craven,
Ghastly, grim and ancient Raven, wandering from the Nightly shore:
Tell me what thy lordly name is on the Night's Plutonian shore!"
>> Quoth the Raven "Nevermore."

Much I marvelled this ungainly fowl to hear discourse so plainly,
Though its answer little meaning—little relevancy bore;

9 For we cannot help agreeing that no living human being
Ever yet was blessed with seeing bird above his chamber door—
Bird or beast upon the sculptured bust above his chamber door—
>> With such name as "Nevermore."

But the Raven, sitting lonely on the **placid** bust, spoke only
That one word, as if his soul in that one word he did outpour.

10 Nothing farther then he uttered, not a feather then he fluttered;
Till I scarcely more than muttered, "Other friends have flown before:
On the morrow *he* will leave me, as my Hopes have flown before."
>> Then the bird said "Nevermore."

Startled at the stillness broken by reply so aptly spoken,
"Doubtless," said I, "what it utters is its only stock and store,

11 Caught from some unhappy master whom unmerciful Disaster
Followed fast and followed faster till his songs one burden bore,
Till the dirges of his Hope that melancholy burden bore
>> Of 'Never—nevermore.' "

But the Raven still **beguiling** all my fancy into smiling,
Straight I wheeled a cushioned seat in front of bird, and bust and door;

12 Then, upon the velvet sinking, I betook myself to linking
Fancy unto fancy, thinking what this **ominous** bird of yore—
What this grim, ungainly, ghastly, **gaunt,** and ominous bird of yore
                                 Meant in croaking "Nevermore."

This I sat engaged in guessing, but no syllable expressing
To the fowl whose fiery eyes now burned into my bosom's core;

13 This and more I sat **divining,** with my head at ease reclining
On the cushion's velvet lining that the lamp-light gloated o'er,
But whose velvet-violet lining with the lamp-light gloating o'er,
                                 She shall press, ah, nevermore!

Then, methought, the air grew denser, perfumed from an unseen censer
Swung by Seraphim whose foot-falls tinkled on the tufted floor.

14 "Wretch," I cried, "thy God hath lent thee—by these angels he hath sent thee
Respite—respite and nepenthe, from thy memories of Lenore!
Quaff, oh quaff this kind nepenthe and forget this lost Lenore!"
                                 Quoth the Raven "Nevermore."

"Prophet!" said I, "thing of evil!—prophet still, if bird or devil!
Whether Tempter sent, or whether tempest tossed thee here ashore,

15 Desolate yet all undaunted, on this desert land enchanted—
On this home by Horror haunted—tell me truly, I implore—
Is there—*is* there **balm** in Gilead?—tell me—tell me, I implore!"
                                 Quoth the Raven "Nevermore."

"Prophet!" said I, "thing of evil!—prophet still, if bird or devil!
By that Heaven that bends above us—by that God we both adore—

16 Tell this soul with sorrow laden if, within the distant Aidenn,
It shall clasp a sainted maiden whom the angels name Lenore—
Clasp a rare and radiant maiden whom the angels name Lenore."
                                 Quoth the Raven "Nevermore."

"Be that word our sign of parting, bird or fiend!" I shrieked, upstarting—
"Get thee back into the tempest and the Night's Plutonian shore!

17 Leave no black plume as a token of that lie thy soul hath spoken!
Leave my loneliness unbroken!—quit the bust above my door!
Take thy beak from out my heart, and take thy form from off my door!"
                                 Quoth the Raven, "Nevermore."

And the Raven, never flitting, still is sitting, *still* is sitting
On the **pallid** bust of Pallas just above my chamber door;

18 And his eyes have all the seeming of a demon's that is dreaming,
And the lamp-light o'er him streaming throws his shadow on the floor;
And my soul from out that shadow that lies floating on the floor
                                 Shall be lifted—nevermore!

                    —Edgar Allan Poe

THINKING IT OVER

(1) Which stanzas make up Part 1? _____

    Part 2? _____

    Part 3? _____

(2) What is the name of the student's dead lover? _____

(3) Which word does Poe continually repeat? _____

    Why does he repeat this word? _____

_____

_____

(4) Who is the "she" Poe refers to in the last line of stanza 13? _____

STUDYING THE PASSAGE

(1) Find the Main Idea: Choose one.
- (a) A conversation between a man and a bird.
- (b) A nocturnal visit.
- (c) How a student's studying is interrupted.
- (d) How a young man is devastated by the death of his lover. _____

(2) Find the Facts: Mark each one *true* or *false*.
- (a) The student is trying to study for an exam. _____
- (b) It is a dark, dreary, windy night. _____
- (c) The raven enters through the door. _____
- (d) The raven perches on a statue. _____
- (e) The student thinks the bird must have escaped from his owner. _____
- (f) The student thinks the bird looks ugly and forbidding. _____
- (g) The student says the bird has been out to make him forget Lenore. _____
- (h) The raven confirms that the young man will never see his lover again. _____

(3) Find the Order: Number the following in the order in which they appear in the passage.
- (a) In there stepped a stately Raven of the saintly days of yore. _____
- (b) 'Tis some visiter entreating entrance at my chamber door. _____
- (c) On the cushion's velvet lining that the lamp-light gloated o'er. _____
- (d) It shall clasp a sainted maiden whom the angels name Lenore. _____
- (e) But the Raven, sitting lonely on the placid bust, spoke only. _____
- (f) While I nodded, nearly napping, suddenly there came a tapping. _____
- (g) And the Raven, never flitting, still is sitting, *still* is sitting. _____
- (h) Deep into that darkness peering, long I stood there wondering, fearing. _____

(4) Go beyond the Facts: What is the raven a symbol of?
- (a) Mournful and neverending remembrance.
- (b) Lenore.
- (c) Guilt.
- (d) Something dreadful that is about to happen. _____

(5) Determine the Writer's Style and Technique: What is the tone of the poem?

    (a) anger

    (b) regret

    (c) frustration

    (d) sadness   _____

USING THE WORDS

(1) Words and Their Meanings: Find the boldfaced word for these definitions.

_____   (a) pleasing greatly; charming; cheating or tricking into doing or believing something wrong

_____   (b) calm and quiet; peaceful

_____   (c) suspension, end; to put an end to

_____   (d) pale; wan; without much color

_____   (e) thin; hungry looking

_____   (f) a bow or curtsey; movement of the body in a token of respect, submission, or reverence

_____   (g) foreboding; foreshadowing evil; being or exhibiting an omen

_____   (h) conformity to accepted standards of behavior

_____   (i) an aromatic (spicy smelling) perfume; a healing or soothing agent

_____   (j) guessing or sensing what another is thinking or feeling

(2) Write a paragraph using four of the words from the list above. Use a separate piece of paper.

WRITING ABOUT IT

Use a separate piece of paper.

(1) Reread the poem, then rewrite it as a narrative, in your own words. Comment on Poe's use of phonetics and descriptive words; his phrasing and rhymes; the repetition of "nevermore" to unify the poem; and Poe's use of symbolism. Finally, discuss the poem's effectiveness.

(2) Write a poem in which you create a certain atmosphere, such as great happiness, deep sorrow, anger, frustration, etc. Use one word repetitively to help create your mood, as Poe uses "nevermore."

ISLAND HOME

ABOUT THE PASSAGE

A remote tropical island becomes the home of a group of boys whose plane crashes during a nuclear war sometime in the future, in William Golding's *Lord of the Flies*. It is not, however, merely the boys' home, it is everyone's home. Golding shows the island to be a miniature version of the world as he sees it.

REASON FOR READING

To notice how Golding describes the boys' new home in terms of the daily rhythm of the tropical island, and how he creates a mood of unreality—as though the boys were living in limbo*—to convey a feeling of universality. The same impression is conveyed in the description of the island as a boat—as if it too were drifting in limbo.

Also notice Golding's exquisite choice of words, his phrasing and rhythmical patterns, and the lyrical quality of his descriptions.

READ THE PASSAGE

The first rhythm that they became used to was the slow swing from dawn to quick dusk. They accepted the pleasures of morning, the bright sun, the whelming sea and sweet air, as a time when play was good and life so full that hope was not necessary and therefore forgotten. Toward noon, as the floods of light fell more nearly to the **perpendicular,** the stark colors of the morning were smoothed in pearl and **opalescence;** and the heat—as though the impending sun's height gave it momentum—became a blow that they ducked, running to the shade and lying there, perhaps even sleeping.

Strange things happened at midday. The glittering sea rose up, moved apart in **planes** of **blatant** impossibility; the coral reef and the few stunted palms that clung to the more elevated parts would float up into the sky, would quiver, be plucked apart, run like raindrops on a wire or be repeated as in an odd succession of mirrors. Sometimes land loomed where there was no land and flicked out like a bubble as the children watched. Piggy discounted all this learnedly as a "mirage"; and since no boy could reach even the reef over the stretch of water where the snapping sharks waited, they grew accustomed

to these mysteries and ignored them, just as they ignored the miraculous, throbbing stars. At midday the illusions merged into the sky and there the sun gazed down like an angry eye. Then, at the end of the afternoon, the mirage subsided and the horizon became level and blue and clipped as the sun declined. That was another time of comparative coolness but **menaced** by the coming of the dark. When the sun sank, darkness dropped on the island like an extinguisher and soon the shelters were full of restlessness, under the remote stars.

The island was roughly boat-shaped; humped near this end with behind them the jumbled descent to the shore. On either side rocks, cliffs, treetops and a steep slope: forward there, the length of the boat, a tamer descent, tree-clad, with hints of pink: and then the jungly flat of the island, dense green, but drawn at the end to a pink tail. There, where the island **petered out** in water, was another island; a rock, almost detached, standing like a fort, facing them across the green with one bold, pink **bastion.**

The boys surveyed all this, then looked out to sea. They were high up and the afternoon had advanced;

* Equivalent to no-man's land, from *Limbo*—a place where some Christians believe people go after death if they do not go to heaven or hell.

From *Lord of the Flies* by William Golding, copyright 1954. Perigee Books, published by The Putnam Publishing Group.

the view was not robbed of sharpness by mirage.

"That's a reef. A coral reef. I've seen pictures like that."

The reef enclosed more than one side of the island, lying perhaps a mile out and parallel to what they now thought of as their beach. The coral was scribbled in the sea as though a giant had bent down to reproduce the shape of the island in a flowing chalk line but tired before he had finished. Inside was peacock water, rocks and weeds showing as in an aquarium; outside was the dark blue of the sea. The tide was running so that long streaks of foam tailed away from the reef and for a moment they felt that the boat was moving steadily **astern.**

THINKING IT OVER

(1) What strange things happened at midday? _____

_____

(2) Choose three phrases or sentences that illustrate Golding's sense of rhythm: _____

_____

_____

_____

(3) Choose five words that you think are particularly effective: _____

_____

STUDYING THE PASSAGE

(1) Find the Main Idea: Choose one.
   (a) What life is like on a tropical island.
   (b) How to survive on a tropical island.
   (c) How the island is like the universe.
   (d) The description of a tropical island. _____

(2) Find the Facts: Mark each one *true* or *false*.
   (a) The best time was in the morning. _____
   (b) They did not worry about being rescued in the morning. _____
   (c) The island became full of bright colors in the intense noontime sun. _____
   (d) It often rained at midday. _____
   (e) There were sharks in the surrounding sea. _____
   (f) With nighttime came restlessness. _____
   (g) There was a rock attached to the island that looked like a church spire. _____
   (h) A reef ran parallel to the beach about a mile out. _____

(3) Find the Order: Number the following in the order in which they appear in the passage.
   (a) Running to the shade and lying there, perhaps even sleeping. _____
   (b) That was another time of comparative coolness. _____
   (c) The coral was scribbled in the sea. _____
   (d) The first rhythm they became used to was the slow swing from dawn to quick dusk. _____
   (e) The boys surveyed all this, then looked out to sea. _____
   (f) On either side rocks, cliffs, treetops and a steep slope. _____
   (g) The tide was running so that long streaks of foam tailed away from the reef. _____
   (h) Or be repeated as in an odd succession of mirrors. _____

(4) Go beyond the Facts: Golding chose a lush, uninhabited tropical island as the home for the boys because of all but one of the following:
   (a) There would be no adults to enforce the socially accepted rules of society.
   (b) There would be plenty of food for the boys and they would not have to worry about shelter.
   (c) To give the feeling of remoteness and nonassociation with the rest of the world.
   (d) He thought the boys would have fun on it.   _____

(5) Determine the Writer's Style and Technique: Which *two* methods does Golding use to describe the island?
   (a) Highly descriptive language.
   (b) Seeing the island through a character's reactions and thoughts.
   (c) Describing the daily changes.
   (d) Describing its weather.   ____   ____

USING THE WORDS

(1) Words and Their Meanings: Find the boldfaced word for these definitions.

   _____ (a) having colors that seem to change and move about, as in an opal

   _____ (b) part of a fort; any strong defense

   _____ (c) at right angles; straight up and down; exactly upright

   _____ (d) very plain or clear

   _____ (e) became smaller and then disappeared

   _____ (f) backward; at or toward the back part of a ship or plane

   _____ (g) flat, level surfaces

   _____ (h) threatened; likely to cause harm

(2) Write a paragraph using four of the words from the list above. Use a separate piece of paper.

WRITING ABOUT IT

Use a separate piece of paper.

Try to copy Golding's method of description. Include imaginative, unusual words, rhythmic phrasing and patterns, and a lyrical quality in your descriptions of the following:

(1) Describe the daily rhythm of your life; write about how you see the dawn, midday, evening, and night-time.

(2) Choose a certain place at a certain time of day and describe it.

THE TURTLE

ABOUT THE PASSAGE

John Steinbeck uses an unusual method to tell his story in *The Grapes of Wrath*. Every other chapter is an "interchapter." These impersonal narratives give background to the other chapters, which tell of the plight of a specific family, the Joads, as they migrate to California to find jobs.

This passage is an example of an interchapter. It is the third chapter in the book (Selection 17 is an excerpt from the first chapter). It continues to establish the main theme symbolically in the form of a turtle, which represents the Joad family's journey to California.

REASON FOR READING

Notice Steinbeck's masterly description of the turtle's minutest movements. See if you can figure out what else the turtle symbolizes and predict what the Joads' journey to California will be like.

READ THE PASSAGE

The concrete highway was edged with a mat of tangled, broken, dry grass, and the grass heads were heavy with oat beards to catch on a dog's coat, and foxtails to tangle in a horse's **fetlocks** and clover burrs to fasten in sheep's wool; sleeping life waiting to be spread and dispersed, every seed armed with an **appliance of dispersal,** twisting darts and parachutes for the wind, little spears and balls of tiny thorns, and all waiting for animals and for the wind, for a man's trouser cuff or the hem of a woman's skirt, all passive but armed with appliances of activity, still, but each possessed of an **anlage** of movement.

The sun lay on the grass and warmed it, and in the shade under the grass the insects moved, ants and ant lions to set traps for them, grasshoppers to jump into the air and flick their yellow wings for a second, sow bugs like little armadillos, plodding restlessly on many tender feet. And over the grass at the roadside a land turtle crawled, turning aside for nothing, dragging his high-domed shell over the grass. His hard legs and yellow-nailed feet **threshed** slowly through the grass, not really walking, but boosting and dragging his shell along. The barley beards slid off his shell, and the clover burrs fell on him and rolled to the ground. His horny beak was partly open, and his fierce, humorous eyes, under brows like fingernails, stared straight ahead. He came over the grass leaving a beaten trail behind him, and the hill, which was the highway **embankment,** reared up ahead of him. For a moment he stopped, his head held high. He blinked and looked up and down. At last he started to climb the embankment. Front clawed feet reached forward but did not touch. The hind feet kicked his shell along, and it scraped on the grass, and on the gravel. As the embankment grew steeper and steeper, the more frantic were the efforts of the land turtle. Pushing hind legs strained and slipped, boosting the shell along, and the horny head protruded as far as the neck could stretch. Little by little the shell slid up the embankment until at last a **parapet** cut straight across its line of march, the shoulder of the road, a concrete wall four inches high. As though they worked independently the hind legs pushed the shell against the wall. The head upraised and peered over the wall to the broad smooth plain of cement. Now the hands, braced on top of the wall, strained and lifted, and the shell came slowly up and rested its front end on the wall. For a moment the turtle rested. A red ant ran into the shell, into the soft skin inside the shell, and suddenly head and legs snapped in, and the **armored** tail clamped in sideways. The red ant was crushed between body and legs. And one head of wild oats was clamped into the shell by a front leg. For a long moment the turtle lay still, and then the neck crept out and the old humorous frowning eyes looked about and the legs and tail came out. The back legs went to work, straining like elephant legs, and the shell tipped to an angle so that the front legs could not reach the level cement plain. But higher and higher the hind legs boosted it, until at last the center of balance was reached, the front tipped down, the front legs scratched at the pavement, and, it was up. But the head of wild oats was held by its stem around the front legs.

Now the going was easy and all the legs worked, and the shell boosted along, waggling from side to side. A sedan driven by a forty-year-old woman approached. She saw the turtle and swung to the right, off the highway, the wheels screamed and a cloud of dust boiled up. Two wheels lifted for a moment and then settled. The car skidded back onto the road, and went on, but more slowly. The turtle had jerked into its shell, but now it hurried on, for the highway was burning hot.

And now a light truck approached, and as it came near, the driver saw the turtle and swerved to hit it. His front wheel struck the edge of the shell, flipped the turtle like a **tiddly-wink,** spun it like a coin, and rolled it off the highway. The truck went back to its course along the right side. Lying on its back, the turtle was tight in its shell for a long time. But at last its legs waved in the air, reaching for something to pull it over. Its front foot caught a piece of quartz and little by little the shell pulled over and flopped upright. The wild oat head fell out and three of the spearhead seeds stuck in the ground. And as the turtle crawled on down the embankment, its shell dragged dirt over the seeds. The turtle entered a dust road and jerked itself along, drawing a wavy shallow trench in the dust with its shell. The old humorous eyes looked ahead, and the horny beak opened a little. His yellow toe nails slipped a fraction in the dust.

THINKING IT OVER

(1) What does the turtle symbolize? _____

(2) What do you think the Joads' journey to California will be like? _____

_____

_____

(3) What was the difference between the woman driver's reaction to seeing the turtle in the road, and the truck

driver's reaction? _____

_____

STUDYING THE PASSAGE

(1) Find the Main Idea: Choose one.
   (a) The dangers of crossing a road..
   (b) Why the turtle crossed the road.
   (c) A turtle crosses a road.
   (d) How a turtle survives.   _____

(2) Find the Facts: Mark each one *true* or *false*.
   (a) The turtle was crossing a dirt road.   _____
   (b) There were a lot of seeds by the road waiting to be taken somewhere.   _____
   (c) The turtle had greenish-brown nails.   _____

(d) The turtle had a horny beak. _____

(e) The turtle had shy, blinking eyes. _____

(f) The turtle had to get up an embankment. _____

(g) The woman skidded off the road trying to avoid the turtle. _____

(h) The truck driver hit the turtle. _____

(3) Find the Order: Number the following in the order in which they appear in the passage.

(a) The front tipped down, the front legs scratched at the pavement, and it was up. _____

(b) Sleeping life waiting to be spread and dispersed. _____

(c) For a moment he stopped, his head held high. _____

(d) The turtle had jerked into its shell, but now it hurried on. _____

(e) Now the hands, braced on top of the wall, strained and lifted. _____

(f) The sun lay on the grass and warmed it. _____

(g) Little by little the shell pulled over and flopped upright. _____

(h) A land turtle crawled, turning aside for nothing, dragging his high-domed shell
over the grass. _____

(4) Go beyond the Facts: What is Steinbeck implying when he says: "The wild oat head fell out and three of the spearhead seeds stuck in the ground. And as the turtle crawled on down the embankment, its shell dragged dirt over the seeds."

(a) The turtle is perpetuating life by planting seeds for new growth.

(b) The turtle is destroying life by burying the seeds.

(c) The turtle is indicating we should hide unpleasant things in life.

(d) It has no special meaning. _____

(5) Determine the Writer's Style and Technique: Which of the following does Steinbeck *not* do in describing the turtle?

(a) Give an extremely realistic description.

(b) Emphasize where and how it moves.

(c) Compare the turtle to other animals.

(d) Show its tenacity—how it will not give up. _____

USING THE WORDS

(1) Words and Their Meanings: Find the boldfaced word for these definitions.

_____ (a) moved about in a violent or jerky way

_____ (b) foundation; rudiment

_____ (c) method of scattering, spreading in different directions

_____ (d) having a hard, protective coating

_____ (e) a long wall of earth, stone, etc. used to hold up a roadway, keep
back water, etc.

_____ (f) tufts of hair on the back of a horse's leg just above the hoof; also
this part of the horse's leg

_____ (g) a small disk that is flipped into a cup in the game of tiddly-winks

_____ (h) a low wall or railing as along a balcony or bridge

(2) Write a paragraph using four of the words from the list above. Use a separate piece of paper.

WRITING ABOUT IT

Use a separate piece of paper.

(1) Describe a situation as Steinbeck does in his interchapters; possibilities include the Great Depression, the Holocaust, or the hurricanes in Hawaii or Florida. Then personalize the situation by describing its impact on a family.

(2) Choose an animal or insect and describe in very realistic detail its journey from one place to another. Remember to focus mainly on its movements, although you should include some details about its appearance, as Steinbeck does.

GREETING CARDS*

ABOUT THE PASSAGE — Greeting cards are an art everyone is familiar with—and many of us couldn't do without. In a few well-chosen words, they express the thoughts and emotions we often find difficult to say ourselves.

REASON FOR READING — To find out more about this specialized art form, and notice how the writer covers specific topics in discussing the history and development of greeting cards.

READ THE PASSAGE

Greeting cards are cards bearing a message suitable for a general occasion, such as a holiday, or for a special personal occasion, such as a birthday, graduation, marriage, promotion, illness, or bereavement. They may also be sent simply to express friendship.

Peoples' need to communicate and their desire to be thoughtful have contributed in great measure to the growth of the custom of sending greeting cards. The greeting card, like a gift, is always selected for another—never kept by the purchaser. Americans exchange an estimated 6 billion greeting cards annually, and the use of cards is increasing throughout the world, particularly in Europe.

Greeting cards can be traced to the written messages that accompanied New Year's gifts in Egypt six centuries before the birth of Christ. In the second century A.D., commemorative medals bearing the inscription "The Senate and People of Rome Wish a Happy and Prosperous New Year to Hadrianus Augustus, the Father of the Country," appeared as another early forerunner of the greeting card.

During the Middle Ages, greeting cards of various types made their appearance in many countries. Woodcuts and engravings were popular in central Europe, and some artisans added color by hand to enhance the beauty of their efforts.

Among the most **venerable** of greeting cards is the valentine. (See more on valentines in Selection 4.)

As love **missives,** valentines were often elaborate, reflecting painstaking effort on the part of their senders. Such books as *The Young Man's Valentine Writer*, published in England in 1797, and *The Quiver of Love*, sold by Marcus Ward and Co. of London as late as 1876, provided verses that could be copied onto handmade valentine greetings. Valentines were first produced commercially in the United States in the 1840s. Their creator, Esther A. Howland, realized sales of $5,000 in the first year.

The most popular greeting card, the Christmas card, was a comparative latecomer. Generally accepted as the first Christmas card was one designed in England in 1835 by the painter John C. Horseley, who created the greeting for Sir Henry Cole. One thousand of the cards were **lithographed** and colored by hand. Within twenty years several British firms were publishing Christmas cards for the general public. Those early efforts were distinguished by the high quality artwork, much of which was supplied by members of the Royal Academy.

The most popular Yuletide greetings of the late 19th century featured flowers, kittens, fairy landscapes, and other subjects without direct Christmas connections. Many were distinguished by attachments such as tiny bells or silk fringe.

In this era, Christmas cards were published in the United States as well. Louis Prang, a German immigrant who became preeminent as a lithographer and color authority, began printing cards in Roxbury, Mass., in 1874, sending his first year's output to England and selling to the American market the following year.

* From the *Encyclopedia Americana*, 1996 Edition. Copyright 1996 by Grolier Incorporated. Reprinted by permission.

Contributing greatly to the growth of the greeting card custom was the evolution of universal and inexpensive postal systems in Europe and in America. It was no longer necessary, as it had been in the 15th century, for example, to depend upon a "common carrier"—a traveler or a soldier who happened to be going in the right direction—to deliver the missive. Finally, establishment of the Universal Postal Union made dispatching a greeting card or letter to any part of the world both easy and inexpensive.

In the United States, in addition to valentines and Christmas cards, greeting cards are available to mark most important holidays or occasions. Evolving from mythology and rites associated with Eostre, the Anglo-Saxon goddess of spring, Easter greetings are among the most popular. Cards for Mother's Day and Saint Patrick's Day appeared about 1912, and Father's Day cards were popular by the 1920's. Thanksgiving, Halloween, Rosh Hashanah, and lesser events are among the holiday occasions for which special greeting cards are available.

Another important side of the greeting card industry is known to its publishers as the "everyday card"—greetings for nonseasonal use. The most important of these is the birthday card. Because of the many possible kinds of approach (sentimental, witty, or humorous) and wide range of price, one major American publisher finds it necessary to maintain a line of more than 1,200 birthday cards from which customers can choose.

The difficulty of expressing one's feelings at a time of a friend's distress led to the use of cheering "get well" cards in the case of illness and of sympathy cards in case of death.

Other year-round greeting card occasions include weddings, wedding anniversaries, and births (both announcements and congratulations). The most popular year-round greetings, however, are friendship cards, which often take the form of little more than a cheery "hello," a printed wish **in lieu of** a face-to-face visit.

The popularity of friendship greetings is responsible for the phenomenal growth of "contemporary" or "studio" cards since their appearance in the mid-1950's. These occasionally zany, sometimes **satirical** cards always embody some offbeat humor, in step with the free, informal attitudes of the 20th century.

Much of the success of greeting cards can be attributed to the fact that most people find it difficult to put their feelings into words. For this reason, because the basic objective of a greeting card is to communicate, the greeting or sentiment is all-important to its success; beauty of design may cause a card to be examined in a store, but the card will not be purchased unless it says what the purchaser wants to say. Verse by such poets as Carl Sandburg, Rudyard Kipling, and Ogden Nash has been used on cards.

To bring the public an unending variety of colorful greetings, publishers use virtually every technique of reproducing upon paper. Lithography, using as many as nine colors to achieve special effects, is the main form of reproduction. Blank **embossing,** steel-die engraving, silk screening, and the application of sequins, glitter, and other materials add **luster** to the cards. Art by Sir Winston Churchill, Salvador Dali, Grandma Moses, and Norman Rockwell, as well as by many of the old masters, has proved popular with card senders.

Greeting cards are produced in the United States by more than 200 publishers, from individuals who create only Christmas greetings to big firms like Hallmark Cards, Inc., of Kansas City, MO. Hallmark has more than 13,000 employees worldwide, including the world's largest art department (some 500 artists) and offers some 14,000 new designs each year. Other important United States greeting card firms include Gibson, Norcross, and American Greetings. Several of the American companies export their cards, but differing social customs, lower price structures, and language barriers have complicated exports. Christmas cards are published in most Christian countries.

Many museums, including the Metropolitan Museum of Art and the Museum of Modern Art in New York, and such institutions as the United Nations (through UNICEF) have entered the greeting card field. They usually offer highly specialized greetings, such as Christmas cards reproducing paintings from museum collections or, in the case of the UNICEF collection, a tableau of international Yuletide customs.

In many ways, greeting cards are a mirror of the times in which they are published, reflecting topical subjects, changing tastes, and current expressions and **idioms.** During the 1960's the characters of Charles Schulz' cartoon *Peanuts*—Snoopy, Charlie Brown, Lucy, and the rest—appeared on greeting cards and achieved popularity unequaled in greeting card history.

THINKING IT OVER

(1) (a) What is the earliest time greeting cards can be traced back to? _____

_____

    (b) In which country was this? _____

(2) What is the most popular kind of greeting card? _____

_____

(3) What development greatly increased the sending of greeting cards? _____

_____

STUDYING THE PASSAGE

(1) Find the Main Idea: Choose one.
    (a) All about the greeting card business.
    (b) The history and development of greeting cards.
    (c) How greeting cards developed into an art form.
    (d) Why we send greeting cards to one another. _____

(2) Find the Facts: Mark each one *true* or *false*.
    (a) Greeting cards developed because of people's need to communicate and their desire to be thoughtful. _____
    (b) Woodcuts and engravings were popular forms of greeting cards in the Middle Ages. _____
    (c) Christmas cards were one of the first greeting cards. _____
    (d) The first Christmas card was created in England. _____
    (e) Mother's Day cards appeared the same year as cards for St. Patrick's Day. _____
    (f) "Contemporary" or "studio" cards always contain humor of some sort. _____
    (g) Lithography is the main form of greeting card reproduction. _____
    (h) Greeting cards mirror the times in which they are created. _____

(3) Find the Order: Number the following in the order in which they appear in the passage.
    (a) Greeting cards are produced in the United States by more than 200 publishers. _____
    (b) It was no longer necessary to depend upon a "common carrier." _____
    (c) The most important of these is the birthday card. _____
    (d) "The Senate and People of Rome Wish a Happy and Prosperous New Year to Hadrianus Augustus." _____
    (e) The popularity of friendship greetings is responsible for the phenomenal growth of "contemporary" or "studio" cards. _____
    (f) Valentines were first produced commercially in the United States in the 1840's. _____
    (g) The greeting card, like a gift, is always selected for another. _____
    (h) In this era, Christmas cards were published in the United States as well. _____

(4) Go beyond the Facts: The incredible success of the greeting card industry is due to which two of the following?

    (a) People care about one another.

    (b) People find it difficult to express their thoughts and emotions in a few words.

    (c) People buy cards because they can't afford other forms of art.

    (d) People think the cards are so beautiful they develop collections of them.   ____ ____

(5) Determine the Writer's Style and Technique: Which of the following is *not* seen in the writer's account:

    (a) A very clear outline, with an orderly progression of ideas.

    (b) Definite topics with appropriate topic sentences.

    (c) Humorous comments.

    (d) Many specific details and facts.   ____

USING THE WORDS

(1) Words and Their Meanings: Find the boldfaced word for these definitions.

_____   (a) phrases or expressions that have a different meaning from what the words suggest in their usual meaning, such as, "to catch one's eye"

_____   (b) decorating with patterns that stand out from the surface

_____   (c) letters or notes

_____   (d) ironic, sarcastic, and humorous

_____   (e) the process of printing from a flat stone or metal plate whose surface is treated so that only the parts having the design will hold ink

_____   (f) gloss; brilliance; brightness

_____   (g) worthy of respect or honor because of old age, fine character, or high rank

_____   (h) in place of

(2) Write a paragraph using four of the words from the list above. Use a separate piece of paper.

WRITING ABOUT IT

Use a separate piece of paper.

(1) The passage discusses several topics on the subject of the history of greeting cards. For example, after the introduction, it talks about the origins of the greeting card, then Valentine's cards, then Christmas cards, and so on. Reread the passage and identify the different topics. Then make an outline of the passage giving the important facts under each heading.

(2) Create a greeting card. Design the cover using cutouts or your own artwork. Then write a message appropriate for the occasion and the person to whom you are giving it.

WILLIAM GOLDING*

ABOUT THE PASSAGE   You have read a sample of William Golding's writing in Selection 22. In this selection you can learn about him.

REASON FOR READING   To learn about William Golding, and to note how a biographical account is written.

READ THE PASSAGE

William Golding has been described as **pessimistic, mythical,** spiritual—an **allegorist** who used his novels as a canvas to paint portraits of man's constant struggle between his civilized self and his hidden, darker nature. The appearance of *Lord of the Flies*, Golding's first published novel, began his career as both a campus cult favorite and one of the late twentieth century's most distinctive—and debated—literary talents. Golding's appeal is summarized by the Nobel Prize Committee, who issued this statement when awarding the author their literature prize in 1983:

"[His] books are very entertaining and exciting. They can be read with pleasure and profit without the need to make much effort with learning or **acumen.** But they have also aroused an unusually great interest in professional literary critics [who find] deep strata of **ambiguity** and complication in Golding's work . . . in which odd people are tempted to reach beyond their limits, thereby being bared to the very marrow."

Comparing his work to that of Jonathan Swift and Herman Melville, the Swedish Academy also said Golding's novels, "with **perspicacity** of realistic narrative art and the universality of myth, illuminate the human condition in the world today."

His novels frequently point out that man is a cruel animal. And individual man, or small groups of men, when taken from their civilized surroundings, confronted by extreme emergency or stripped of the trappings of modern civilization, invariably turn savage. His novels convey this message in a manner that turns it to fable.

William Gerald Golding was born in a small hamlet in Cornwall, in the southwestern part of England, in 1911. He died near there in June, 1993, at the age of 81. His father was a schoolmaster and his mother was active in the movement to win voting rights for women.

Golding went to the local high school and, apparently, tried his hand at writing even then. He then went to Oxford University to study science, but after two years he changed to English literature. He concentrated particularly on Anglo-Saxon language and literature and lists the anonymous Anglo-Saxon author of *The Battle of Maldon* as one of the major literary influences on him.

Golding graduated from Oxford in 1934 with a B.A. degree. A year before, at the age of twenty-two, he published his first literary work—a slim volume of poetry. In hindsight the author called the poems, "poor, thin things," but Stephen Medcalf, in his biography of Golding, says, "They are not bad. They deal with emotions—as they come out in the poems, rather easy emotions—of loss and grief, reflected in nature and the seasons."

After graduating, Golding perpetuated family tradition by becoming a schoolmaster. However, his teaching career was interrupted in 1940 by World War II. "Schoolie," as he was called, served five years in the Royal Navy. He saw active duty in the North Atlantic, commanding a rocket launching craft. Present at the sinking of the *Bismarck*, and participating in the D-Day invasion, Golding later recalled: "World War II was the turning point for me. I began to see what people were capable of doing. Anyone who moved through those years without understanding that man produces evil as a bee produces honey must have been blind or wrong in the head."

After the war, Golding devoted himself to teaching and writing. He produced three novel manuscripts that remained unpublished. Then, in 1954, he created *Lord of the Flies*. The novel was rejected by twenty-one publishers before Faber & Faber accepted it. At first it received mixed critical reaction, but it rapidly became very popular and was soon recognized as a major work of art. The book has since been translated into twenty-six languages and millions of copies have been sold. It became a popular text in schools, as the King of Sweden noted when he presented Golding's Nobel Prize to him. "It is a great pleasure to meet you, Mr. Golding. I had to do *Lord of the Flies* at school," he said.

That was one of the reasons that Golding's Nobel Prize took some by surprise and even offended others. One Nobel judge even held a news conference to say that Golding was not truly up to Nobel standards. But other judges disagreed.

Though Golding's other works never brought him the vast readership of *Lord of the Flies*, his books sold consistently. His 1980 novel, *Rites of Passage*, won the Booker Prize, Britain's premier book award.

Rites tells of a 19th-century voyage to Australia and how a pompous **man of the cloth** becomes caught up in sexual scandal before dying disgraced. A sequel to that novel, *Close Quarters*, was published in 1987, with *Fire Down Below* finishing the trilogy in 1989.

His other novels included *The Inheritors*, from 1955, which he once described as his favorite; it told of the **annihilation** of Neanderthal people by Homo sapiens. He also wrote *Pincher Martin*, a 1956 novel describing the agonies of a drowning seaman; *Free Fall* (1959); *The Spire* (1964); *The Pyramid* (1967); *The Scorpion God* (1971); and *Darkness Visible* (1979).

He also wrote the 1958 play *The Brass Butterfly* and collections of essays such as *The Hot Gates* (1965). His 1984 novel, *The Paper Men*, told of the pursuit of a famous, if reclusive, English novelist by a brassy American academician. Some critics saw more than a little parallel between the "novelist" and the novelist. One recalled Golding's irritation at becoming "the raw material of an academic light industry."

In 1988, Golding received his country's highest possible honor: he was knighted by the Queen. Until he died in 1993, Sir William (as he was now called) continued writing and enjoying his hobbies, which he once listed as "thinking, classical Greek, sailing, archeology, and playing the piano and various other musical instruments." His last novel, *The Double Tongue*, was published posthumously in 1995.

THINKING IT OVER

(1) Describe three special honors Golding received: _____

_____

_____

(2) When did Golding live? _____

(3) What did the King of Sweden tell Golding? _____

_____

(4) Which is Golding's favorite novel? _____

STUDYING THE PASSAGE

(1) Find the Main Idea: Choose one.
   (a) Why Golding wrote the way he did.
   (b) The effect of World War II on Golding.
   (c) An account of Golding's life.
   (d) A review of Golding's books.   _____

(2) Find the Facts: Mark each one *true* or *false*.
   (a) Not everyone agrees that Golding's works are good literature.   _____
   (b) It has been said that you don't have to be well-educated to enjoy Golding's books.   _____
   (c) Golding's works have been compared to those by Poe because they deal with evil.   _____
   (d) Golding was 81 when he died.   _____
   (e) *Rites* tells about a voyage to America.   _____
   (f) *Pincher Martin* describes the horrors of war.   _____
   (g) Golding's last literary work was *The Paper Men* in 1984.   _____
   (h) Being famous sometimes annoyed Golding.   _____

(3) Find the Order: Number the following in the order in which they appear in the passage.
   (a) But other judges disagreed.   _____
   (b) He concentrated particularly on Anglo-Saxon language and literature.   _____
   (c) It became a popular text in schools.   _____
   (d) An allegorist who uses his novels as a canvas to paint portraits of man's
       constant struggle . . .   _____
   (e) Some critics saw more than a little parallel between the "novelist"
       and the novelist.   _____
   (f) He saw active duty in the North Atlantic.   _____
   (g) His novels frequently point out that man is a cruel animal.   _____
   (h) *Rites of Passage* won the Booker Prize.   _____

(4) Go beyond the Facts: Which one of the following does *not* describe Golding's books?
   (a) Controversial.
   (b) Pessimistic.
   (c) More to them than meets the eye.
   (d) Amusing.   _____

(5) Determine the Writer's Style and Technique: Which *two* does the writer do in telling about Golding?
   (a) Analyzes each of his books.
   (b) Tells about his home life.
   (c) Mentions key events in his life.
   (d) Gives some clues as to how Golding came to view life.   _____ _____

USING THE WORDS

(1) Words and Their Meanings: Find the boldfaced word for these definitions.

_____   (a) shrewdness; keenness and speed in understanding and dealing with a situation

_____   (b) having acute mental vision or discernment

_____   (c) one who uses allegories, stories with both obvious and hidden meanings

_____   (d) clergyman

_____   (e) feeling that there is more evil than good in life; feeling gloomy about life

_____   (f) complete destruction

_____   (g) in, of, or like a myth; imaginary, not real

_____   (h) the state of being unclear or indefinite

(2) Write a paragraph using four of the words from the list above. Use a separate piece of paper.

WRITING ABOUT IT

Use a separate piece of paper.

(1) Write a biographical account of an author whose book you are studying in class. As well as giving significant events in the author's life, include a description of the general characteristics and themes of his or her writings and mention other works he or she has published.

(2) Golding says humans are innately evil. Argue that this is not so—humans are innately good. Give specific examples from real life and fiction to prove your point.